I. I. Hirschman, Jr.

Washington University

Infinite Series

HOLT, RINEHART AND WINSTON

New York

Preface

This pamphlet on infinite series, although intended as a textbook, has also been designed to be used in applied courses beyond the advanced calculus level as a convenient and inexpensive source for standard results of analysis. Although the treatment throughout is completely rigorous, emphasis has been placed upon the application of the theory developed rather than upon the theory itself. Thus there is more material than usual on the problems of computation with series, and there are many applications, particularly to the theory of special functions.

Since it is a textbook, many problems have been included. In the earlier chapters they are primarily computational. In the later chapters they often afford a brief introduction to material not contained in the text itself.

Chapter 1 contains the elementary theory of infinite series. In Chapters 2 and 3 there is a relatively complete exposition of the basic properties of Taylor series and Fourier series. Chapter 4 deals with series of functions and the applications of uniform convergence. Chapter 5 concerns itself with double series, changes in the order of summation, and summability. In Chapter 6 the results of Chapters 4 and 5 are applied to give a systematic treatment of real power series and real analytic functions. In Chapter 7 the earlier treatment of Fourier series is completed by a discussion of several more advanced topics such as summability, Parseval's equality, and the convolution theorem.

The following notations from elementary set theory will be employed. A set U is a well-determined collection of (mathematical) objects. Sets are sometimes defined by verbal sentences but often by formulas such as[1]

$$ A = \{(x, y) \mid x^2 + y^2 \le 1\}, \qquad B = \{(x, y) \mid x \ge 0\}. $$

The first of these relations is to be read "A is the set of all pairs (of real numbers) such that $x^2 + y^2 \le 1$." Since A and B are subsets of the Cartesian plane they

[1] Sometimes, when there is no possibility of confusion, these formulas may be somewhat shortened. For example we might write $A = \{x^2 + y^2 \le 1\}$.

can be graphed. In Figs. A and B below the shaded points belong to the sets in question.

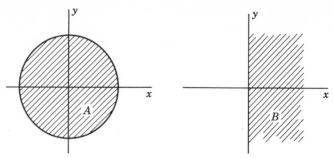

Figs. A and B

The notation $u \in U$ means that u is one of the elements of the set U; $u \notin U$ means that u is not an element of U. For example, $(\frac{1}{2}, \frac{1}{2}) \in A$, $(2, 3) \notin A$. Given two sets U_1 and U_2, we defined $U_1 \cup U_2$ by the formula

$$U_1 \cup U_2 = \{u \mid u \in U_1 \text{ or } u \in U_2\}.$$

In words $U_1 \cup U_2$ consists of all elements which belong to U_1 or to U_2 or to both U_1 and U_2. Again

$$U_1 \cap U_2 = \{u \mid u \in U_1 \text{ and } u \in U_2\}.$$

In words $U_1 \cap U_2$ consists of all the elements that belong to both U_1 and U_2. We illustrate these operations using A and B in Fig. C. The symbol \varnothing is reserved

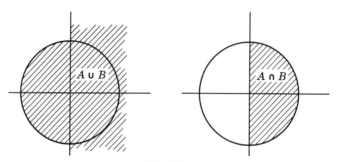

Fig. C

for the empty set which has no elements. Thus $U_1 \cap U_2 = \varnothing$ means that U_1 and U_2 have no elements in common. We write $U_1 \subset U_2$ if every element of U_1 is also an element of U_2. Thus $U_1 \subset U_2$ if and only in $U_1 \cup U_2 = U_2$. Note that $U_1 \cap U_2 \subset U_1$ holds for every U_1 and U_2.

The following sets are used so frequently that special letters are reserved for them:

\mathfrak{R} is the set of all real numbers x $(-\infty < x < \infty)$;

\mathfrak{P} is the set of all nonnegative integers n $(n = 0, 1, \cdots)$;

\mathfrak{P}_1 is the set of all positive integers n $(n = 1, 2, \cdots)$.

Later some other sets which occur frequently will be assigned special letters. See in this connection the index of special symbols, page 173.

See in this connection the index of special symbols, page 173.

I. I. H.

St. Louis, Missouri
December, 1961

Contents

Infinite Series

[1]

Tests for Convergence and Divergence

1. Sequences

Since infinite series are studied by means of sequences, this first section is devoted to a very brief review of sequences. An infinite sequence is simply a succession of numbers,

$$s_1, s_2, s_3, \cdots ,$$

indexed by consecutive integers. Here the "\cdots" always written in just this way stands for the remaining terms: s_4, s_5, etc., s_n being the term of index n. Alternatively we can write

$$s_n \quad (n = 1, 2, \cdots) \quad \text{or} \quad \{s_n\}_{n=1}^{\infty} .$$

A sequence need not begin with the term of index 1 but may start with any index. In more technical language a sequence whose initial index is m,

$$t_m, t_{m+1}, t_{m+2}, \cdots ,$$

is a real valued function on the set $(m, m + 1, m + 2, \cdots)$, the value of this function at n being t_n.

We shall be particularly concerned with limits. In the first part of this section our discussion will be somewhat informal. A parallel formal development of this same subject is given Sec. 1* which follows.

DEFINITION 1a. Let s_n $(n = 1, 2, \cdots)$ be a sequence. We say that the limit of the sequence s_n $(n = 1, 2, \cdots)$ is s, equivalently $\lim_{n \to \infty} s_n = s$, if s_n is arbitrarily close to s for all sufficiently large n.

For example,

$$\lim_{n \to \infty} \frac{2^n}{1 + 2^n} = 1 ,$$

$$\lim_{n \to \infty} \left(2 + \frac{4}{n} \right) = 2 .$$

Some sequences do not have limits; for example, the sequences

$$\{(-1)^n\}_0^{\infty}, \quad \text{i.e.,} \quad 1, -1, 1, -1, \cdots ,$$

1

and

$$\{2^n\}_0^\infty, \qquad \text{i.e.,} \qquad 1, 2, 4, 8, \cdots,$$

do not have limits. When limits exist, they may be combined in various ways. The following discussion includes only a few of these ways, but these few are so important that they deserve special attention. Let

$$s_1, s_2, s_3, \cdots$$

be a sequence and c a constant. Then from these ingredients we can manufacture a new sequence whose terms are

$$cs_1, cs_2, cs_3, \cdots .$$

THEOREM 1b. If $\lim\limits_{n\to\infty} s_n$ exists, then $\lim\limits_{n\to\infty} cs_n$ exists, and

$$\lim_{n\to\infty} cs_n = c \lim_{n\to\infty} s_n .$$

To see this, imagine that $\lim\limits_{n\to\infty} s_n = 7$ and $c = 2$. Then for n very large, s_n is very near 7, and therefore $2s_n$ is very near 14.

Again given two sequences (with the same initial index)

$$s_1, s_2, s_3, \cdots ,$$

$$t_1, t_2, t_3, \cdots ,$$

we can form a new sequence whose terms are

$$s_1 + t_1, s_2 + t_2, s_3 + t_3, \cdots .$$

THEOREM 1c. If $\lim\limits_{n\to\infty} s_n$ and $\lim\limits_{n\to\infty} t_n$ exist, so does $\lim\limits_{n\to\infty} (s_n + t_n)$ and $\lim\limits_{n\to\infty} (s_n + t_n) = \lim\limits_{n\to\infty} s_n + \lim\limits_{n\to\infty} t_n$.

Again, if one thinks of a special case, this result becomes obvious. For example suppose that $\lim\limits_{n\to\infty} s_n = 7$, $\lim\limits_{n\to\infty} t_n = 11$. Then if n is very large, s_n is close to 7 and t_u is close to 11, and thus $s_n + t_n$ is close to 18.

THEOREM 1d. If $\lim\limits_{n\to\infty} s_n$ and $\lim\limits_{n\to\infty} t_n$ exist, so does $\lim\limits_{n\to\infty} s_n t_n$ and $\lim\limits_{n\to\infty} s_n t_n = (\lim\limits_{n\to\infty} s_n) (\lim\limits_{n\to\infty} t_n)$.

THEOREM 1e. If $\lim\limits_{n\to\infty} s_n = s$ and $s \neq 0$, then $\lim\limits_{n\to\infty} 1/s_n = 1/s$.

A moment's reflection shows that these results too are intuitively obvious.

PROBLEMS

1. (a) If in the sequence

$$0, 3, 8, 15, 24, 35, \cdots$$

"0" is counted as the term of index 2, what is the term of index 5?

(b) If $s_n = (n^2 + 1)^{-1}$ $(n = 2, 3, \cdots)$, what is the term of index $2n + 1$?

In each of the following problem state whether the indicated sequence has a limit, and give the limit when it exists.

2. (a) $r_n = \dfrac{n - 1}{n + 1} \cdots$ $\qquad (n = 3, 4, \cdots)$.

(b) $s_n = \dfrac{n^2 + 4}{n + 2}$ $\qquad (n = 1, 2, \cdots)$.

(c) $t_n = \dfrac{2^n}{n^2}$ $\qquad (n = 1, 2, \cdots)$.

3. (a) $a_n = \log_e \log_e n$ $\qquad (n = 8, 9, 10, \cdots)$.

(b) $b_n = \dfrac{e^{-n} + 1}{e^n}$ $\qquad (n = 0, 1, 2, \cdots)$.

(c) $c_n = \dfrac{(-5)^n + 4^n}{5^n}$ $\qquad (n = 1, 2, \cdots)$.

4. (a) $r_n = \sin\left(\dfrac{\pi n}{3}\right)$ $\qquad (n = 0, 1, 2, \cdots)$.

(b) $s_n = \dfrac{5n + \cos(n\pi)}{n - 2}$ $\qquad (n = 3, 4, \cdots)$.

(c) $t_n = \text{Arctan } n^2$ $\qquad (n = 0, 1, \cdots)$.

5. (a) $a_n = \dfrac{n!}{4^n}$ $\qquad (n = 0, 1, \cdots)$.

(b) $b_n = \dfrac{(n!)^2}{(2n)!}$ $\qquad (n = 1, 2, \cdots)$.

1*. Limits

In Sec. 1 the relation $\lim\limits_{n \to \infty} s_n = s$ was informally defined. This definition was then amplified by some examples. In the present section we shall state the definition of limit precisely.

DEFINITION 1a. Let s_n $(n = 1, 2, \cdots)$ be a sequence. We write $\lim\limits_{n \to \infty} s_n = s$ if for each positive number $\epsilon > 0$ there is an integer N, depending on ϵ and on $(s_n)_1^\infty$, such that $|s_n - s| < \epsilon$ if $n \geq N$.

This definition is, of course, nothing more than a precise statement of the informal definition given in Sec. 1. The latter asserts that s_n will be arbitrarily close to s if n is large enough. Take an $\epsilon > 0$. A natural measure of closeness is

to require that s_n be within ϵ of s; that is, $|s_n - s| < \epsilon$. To say that s_n must be "this close" to s if n is "large enough" is just to say that there must be some integer N such that $|s_n - s| < \epsilon$ if $n \geq N$. Finally *if* s_n is to be "arbitrarily close" to s if n is large enough, we must be able to find an N for each positive ϵ. This however is just Definition 1a.

We recall that the relation $\lim\limits_{n \to \infty} s_n = s$ may also be expressed by saying that the sequence s_n has the limit s. Not every sequence has a limit, of course.

EXAMPLE 1. Prove that

(1) $$\lim_{n \to \infty} \frac{(2n^2 + 1)^2}{n^4} = 4 .$$

We have $(2n^2 + 1)^2/n^4 = 4 + 4/n^2 + 1/n^4$. Given $\epsilon > 0$, let us choose N so large that $5/N^2 < \epsilon$. If $n \geq N$, then

$$\left| \left(4 + \frac{4}{n^2} + \frac{1}{n^4}\right) - 4 \right| = \frac{4}{n^2} + \frac{1}{n^4} = \left(4 + \frac{1}{n^2}\right)\frac{1}{n^2}$$

$$\leq \frac{5}{n^2} \leq \frac{5}{N^2} < \epsilon .$$

Now that a precise definition of limit has been given, it is possible to *prove* the theorems of Sec. 1 which were justified there only by an appeal to intuition.

THEOREM 1b. If $\lim\limits_{n \to \infty} s_n = s$, then $\lim\limits_{n \to \infty} cs_n = cs$.

Proof. If $c = 0$, our conclusion is trivial; we may therefore restrict our attention to the case $c \neq 0$. Let $\epsilon > 0$ be given. We shall prove that there exists an integer N such that if $n \geq N$, then $|cs_n - cs| < \epsilon$. To do this, let $\delta = \epsilon/|c|$. Since $\delta > 0$, there is by assumption an integer N such that $|s_n - s| < \delta$ if $n \geq N$. If $n \geq N$, then

$$|cs_n - cs| = |c| \, |s_n - s| < |c| \, \delta = \epsilon ,$$

as desired.

THEOREM 1c. If $\lim\limits_{n \to \infty} s_n = s$ and if $\lim\limits_{n \to \infty} t_n = t$, then $\lim\limits_{n \to \infty} (s_n + t_n) = s + t$.

First Proof. Let $\epsilon > 0$ be given. Since $\epsilon/2 > 0$, there exists by assumption an integer N_1 such that $|s_n - s| < \epsilon/2$ if $n \geq N_1$, and there exists an integer N_2 such that $|t_n - t| < \epsilon/2$ if $n \geq N_2$. (We could, as in the proof of Theorem 1a, set $\epsilon/2 = \delta$ etc., but the proof is just as clear and slightly shorter without this.) Let N be the greater of N_1 and N_2, $N = \max(N_1, N_2)$. If $n \geq N$, then $n \geq N_1$ and $n \geq N_2$. Consequently if $n \geq N$,

$$|(s_n + t_n) - (s + t)| = |(s_n - s) + (t_n - t)|$$
$$\leq |s_n - s| + |t_n - t|$$
$$< \frac{\epsilon}{2} + \frac{\epsilon}{2} = \epsilon ,$$

as desired.

Second Proof. Let $\epsilon > 0$ be given. By assumption there exists an integer N_1 such that $|s_n - s| < 4\epsilon/5$ if $n \geq N_1$ and an integer N_2 such that $|s_n - s| < \epsilon/5$ if $n \geq N_2$. Let $N = \max(N_1, N_2)$. If $n \geq N$, then

$$|(s_n + t_n) - (s + t)| \leq |s_n - s| + |t_n - t| < \frac{4\epsilon}{5} + \frac{\epsilon}{5} = \epsilon.$$

The reason for the inclusion here of this second proof is to throw into relief the underlying idea.

THEOREM 1d. *If* $\lim\limits_{n\to\infty} s_n = s$ *and if* $\lim\limits_{n\to\infty} t_n = t$, *then* $\lim\limits_{n\to\infty} s_n t_n = st$.

Proof. Let us choose a constant r such that $r > |s|$, $r > |t|$. Since $\lim\limits_{n\to\infty} s_n = s$, there is an integer N_1 such that $|s_n| < r$ if $n \geq N_1$. Next given $\epsilon > 0$, there is an integer N_2 such that $|s_n - s| < \epsilon/2r$ if $n \geq N_2$, and there is an integer N_3 such that $|t_n - t| < \epsilon/2r$ if $n \geq N_3$. Let $N = \max(N_1, N_2, N_3)$. We assert that $|s_n t_n - st| < \epsilon$ if $n \geq N$. To see this note that

$$
\begin{aligned}
|s_n t_n - st| &= |s_n t_n - s_n t + s_n t - st| \\
&\leq |s_n t_n - s_n t| + |s_n t - st| = |s_n||t_n - t| + |t||s_n - s| \\
&< r|t_n - t| + r|s_n - s| \qquad\qquad \text{since } n \geq N_1 \\
&< r\left(\frac{\epsilon}{2r}\right) + r\left(\frac{\epsilon}{2r}\right) = \epsilon \qquad \text{since } n \geq N_2, n \geq N_3.
\end{aligned}
$$

THEOREM 1e. *If* $\lim\limits_{n\to\infty} s_n = s$ *and* $s \neq 0$, *then* $\lim\limits_{n\to\infty} 1/s_n = 1/s$.

Proof. Let us chose a constant r $(0 < r < |s|)$. Since $\lim\limits_{n\to\infty} s_n = s$, there is an integer N_1 such that $|s_n| > r$ if $n \geq N_1$. Next given $\epsilon > 0$, there is an integer N_2 such that $|s_n - s| < r^2\epsilon$ if $n \geq N_2$. Let $N = \max(N_1, N_2)$; then

$$
\begin{aligned}
\left|\frac{1}{s_n} - \frac{1}{s}\right| = \left|\frac{s - s_n}{s_n s}\right| &= \frac{|s_n - s|}{|s_n||s|} \\
&< \frac{|s_n - s|}{r^2} \qquad\qquad \text{since } n \geq N_1 \\
&< \frac{(\epsilon r^2)}{r^2} = \epsilon \qquad\qquad \text{since } n \geq N_2,
\end{aligned}
$$

as desired.

PROBLEMS

In the following problems you are permitted to use (and should use) the theorems of Sec. 1*.

1. Prove that if $\lim\limits_{n\to\infty} s_n = s$, $\lim\limits_{n\to\infty} t_n = t$, and if $t \neq 0$, then $\lim\limits_{n\to\infty} (s_n/t_n) = s/t$.

2. (a) Prove by induction that if m is any positive integer, then $\lim\limits_{n\to\infty} s = s$ implies that $\lim\limits_{n\to\infty} (s_n)^m = s^m$.

(b) Deduce that if $P(x) = a_0 + a_1 x + \cdots + a_m x^m$ is any polynomial, then $\lim\limits_{n\to\infty} s_n = s$ implies that $\lim\limits_{n\to\infty} P(s_n) = P(s)$.

3. Prove that if $\lim\limits_{n\to\infty} s_n = s$ and if $s_0 \le s_1 \le s_2 \cdots$, then $s_n \le s$ for $n = 0, 1, \cdots$.

4. Prove that if $s_n \le t_n$ for $n = 0, 1, \cdots$, and if $\lim\limits_{n\to\infty} s_n = s$, $\lim\limits_{n\to\infty} t_n = t$, then $s \le t$. Deduce that if $s_n \le M$ ($n = 0, 1, \cdots$) and if $\lim\limits_{n\to\infty} s_n = s$, then $s \le M$.

5. Let $\lim\limits_{n\to\infty} s_n = 0$. Prove that if $\alpha > 0$, then $\lim\limits_{n\to\infty} s_n^\alpha = 0$ too. HINT: Given $\epsilon > 0$, let $\delta = \epsilon^{1/\alpha}$; then chose N so large that $|s_n| < \delta$ for $n \ge N$, etc.

2. Convergence

Almost everyone knows that

(1) $$\text{“}\tfrac{1}{2} + \tfrac{1}{4} + \tfrac{1}{8} + \tfrac{1}{16} + \cdots = 1.\text{”}$$

However since one cannot add infinitely many numbers in the way in which one adds finitely many numbers, the relation **(1)** is evidently not exactly comparable to the relation

(2) $$1 + 3 + 5 = 9.$$

To see what **(1)** means, consider the table of *partial sums:*

$$\tfrac{1}{2},$$
$$\tfrac{1}{2} + \tfrac{1}{4} = \tfrac{3}{4},$$
$$\tfrac{1}{2} + \tfrac{1}{4} + \tfrac{1}{8} = \tfrac{7}{8},$$
$$\tfrac{1}{2} + \tfrac{1}{4} + \tfrac{1}{8} + \tfrac{1}{16} = \tfrac{15}{16},$$
$$\vdots$$

From this we see that as we add more and more terms from **(1)**, the partial sums so obtained become closer and closer to 1 the further out we go. This is of course what **(1)** really means, and it suggests the right definition for the general case.

Consider the infinite series

(3) $$u_1 + u_2 + u_3 + \cdots$$

From the *series* we form the *sequence* of partial sums

$$s_1 = u_1,$$
$$s_2 = u_1 + u_2,$$
$$s_3 = u_1 + u_2 + u_3,$$
$$\vdots$$

DEFINITION 2a. The series (**3**) is said to converge to the sum s if $\lim\limits_{n\to\infty} s_n = s$. In this case we write

$$\sum_{n=1}^{\infty} u_n = s .$$

The reader should immediately note one important difference between infinite series (infinite sums) and finite series (finite sums). Every finite series such as (**2**) has a sum, but only some infinite series have sums since $\lim\limits_{n\to\infty} s_n$ may not exist. This possibility is taken care of by the following definition:

DEFINITION 2b. The series (**3**) is said to diverge if $\lim\limits_{n\to\infty} s_n$ does not exist. In this case we write $\sum_{n=1}^{\infty} u_n$ does not exist.

Clearly any infinite series either converges or diverges.

An example of a divergent series is

(**4**) $$1 + 1 + 1 + \cdots .$$

If the first term of this series is assigned the index 1, then $s_n = n$, and there is no finite number s such that s_n becomes closer and closer to s as n becomes larger and larger.

In the series (**3**), u_n is "the term of index n." A series need not start with the terms of index 1; for example the series

(**5**) $$u_3 + u_4 + u_5 + \cdots ,$$

(**6**) $$v_0 + v_1 + v_2 + \cdots ,$$

start with the terms of index 3 and index 0, respectively. We shall always use the convention that the partial sum of index n for a given series is the sum of the terms from the beginning through the term of index n. Thus the partial sum of index 4 for the series (**5**) is $u_3 + u_4$, whereas for the series (**6**) it is $v_0 + v_1 + v_2 + v_3 + v_4$. We shall also have occasion to use notations such as

$$\sum_{n=3}^{\infty} u_n , \qquad \sum_{r=0}^{\infty} v_r .$$

These are simply new ways of writing (**5**) and (**6**).

We conclude this section by examining one special series where $u_n = ar^n$,

(**7**) $$\sum_{0}^{\infty} ar^n .$$

This series is called the *geometric series*. Note, however, that it is not one series but rather a family of series, one series for each assignment of a and r. We shall

assume throughout that $a \neq 0$ since otherwise every term of (**7**) is 0 and the series converges trivially. Consider the multiplication:

$$
\begin{array}{l}
1 + r + \cdots + r^n \\
1 - r
\end{array}
$$

$$
\begin{array}{l}
1 + r + r^2 + \cdots + r^n \\
\quad - r - r^2 - \cdots - r^n - r^{n+1}
\end{array}
$$

$$
1 \hspace{5cm} - r^{n+1} \, ,
$$

the result of which may be written as

$$
(1 - r)(1 + r + r^2 + \cdots + r^n) = (1 - r^{n+1}).
$$

If r is different from 1, we may divide by $1 - r$ to find that

$$
(1 + r + r^2 + \cdots + r^n) = \frac{1 - r^{n+1}}{1 - r} \, .
$$

Since s_n, the partial sum of index n of the series (**7**), is

$$
s_n = a + ar + \cdots + ar^n \, ,
$$

we find that

(**8**) $$ s_n = \frac{a(1 - r^{n+1})}{1 - r} \qquad (r \neq 1) \, . $$

If $-1 < r < 1$, then r^{n+1} approaches 0 as $n \to \infty$, and thus $\lim\limits_{n \to \infty} s_n = a/(1 - r)$. If $r < -1$ or $r > 1$, it is evident from (**8**) that $\lim\limits_{n \to \infty} s_n$ does not exist. The formula (**8**) is not valid if $r = 1$; however, if $r = 1$, then $s_n = (n + 1)$, and $\lim\limits_{n \to \infty} s_n$ does not exist.

THEOREM 2c. If $-1 < r < 1$, the geometric series (**7**) is convergent to the sum $a/(1 - r)$. For all other values of r it is divergent.

Note the series (**1**) is the special case $a = 1$, $r = \frac{1}{2}$.

PROBLEMS

1. What is the partial sum of index 3 of the series $\sum_{n=0}^{\infty} 1/(n^2 + 1)$? Give the answer in decimal form correct to within one unit in the third place after the decimal. NOTE: Use four or five places in the computations, and round off to three places at the end.

2. What is the partial sum of index 20 of the series $\sum_{n=1}^{\infty} n^{-1}$? Give the answer in decimal form correct to within one unit in the second decimal place. NOTE: Use four places in the computations, and round off to two places at the end.

Determine whether the following geometric series are convergent or divergent. If a series is convergent, find its sum.

3. $\sum_{n=0}^{\infty} 2(-\frac{1}{2})^n$.

4. $\frac{1}{10} + \frac{2}{10} + \frac{4}{10} + \cdots$.

5. $\sum_{n=1}^{\infty} (10)^{-n}$.

6. $- 6 + 2 - \frac{2}{3} + \cdots$.

7. $\sum_{n=0}^{\infty} 3 \left(\frac{2}{3}\right)^{-n}$.

8. Evaluate the repeating decimal $0.181818 \cdots$.

HINT: This can be written as

$$\frac{18}{100} + \frac{18}{100} \left(\frac{1}{100}\right) + \frac{18}{100} \left(\frac{1}{100}\right)^2 + \cdots .$$

The answer should be given as a rational number.

9. Evaluate the repeating decimal $2.702702702 \cdots$.

10. Evaluate the repeating decimal $98.198198198 \cdots$.

The following two series have the property that a *simple* explicit formula exists in both cases for the partial sum of index n. This formula can be guessed after actually computing the first few partial sums. In each case find this formula, and use it to determine if the series in question is divergent or convergent. If it is convergent, give its sum.

11. $\sum_{1}^{\infty} \frac{1}{k(k + 1)}$.

12. $\sum_{1}^{\infty} \log\left(1 + \frac{1}{k}\right)$.

3. Some Preliminary Results

The section is devoted to a few simple but very useful general facts concerning series.

THEOREM 3a. If $\sum_{1}^{\infty} u_k = s$, then $\sum_{1}^{\infty} cu_k = cs$.

Proof. Let s_n and t_n be the partial sums of index n of the two series above. Then $s_n = u_1 + u_2 + \cdots + u_n$, $t_n = cu_1 + cu_2 + \cdots + cu_n$, and thus $t_n = cs_n$. By Theorem 1b

$$\sum_1^\infty cu_k = \lim_{n\to\infty} t_n = c \lim_{n\to\infty} s_n = cs.$$

THEOREM 3b. If $\displaystyle\sum_1^\infty u_k = s$ and $\displaystyle\sum_1^\infty v_k = t$, then $\displaystyle\sum_1^\infty u_k + v_k = s + t$.

Proof. Left to the reader.

THEOREM 3c. The addition or removal of a finite number of terms at the beginning of an infinite series does not change its convergence or divergence.

Proof. We shall consider one simple case. Suppose that $\sum_{n=0}^\infty u_n$ converges; we shall prove that $\sum_{n=2}^\infty u_n$ also converges. Let

$$s_n = u_0 + u_1 + u_2 + \cdots + u_n ,$$

$$t_n = \qquad\qquad u_2 + \cdots + u_n ,$$

be the partial sums of index n for the two series in question; then $t_n = -(u_0 + u_1) + s_n$. By Theorem 1c

$$\sum_{n=2}^\infty u_n = \lim_{n\to\infty} t_n = -(u_0 + u_1) + \lim_{n\to\infty} s_n = -(u_0 + u_1) + \sum_{n=0}^\infty u_n .$$

Thus we have proved not only that the second series converges but that its sum is the sum of the first series less $(u_0 + u_1)$.

We shall frequently have occasion to make the following application of Theorem 3c. Given the series

(1)
$$\sum_{n=0}^\infty u_n ,$$

let s_N be the partial sum of index N

$$s_N = \sum_0^\infty u_n .$$

Let us further define

(2)
$$R_N = \sum_{N+1}^\infty u_n .$$

Theorem 3c shows that the infinite series (1) and (2) both converge or both diverge and that in the former case

$$\sum_0^\infty u_n = s_N + R_N.$$

The notation (2) is standard.

THEOREM 3d. If the series $\sum_0^\infty u_k$ converges, then $\lim_{n \to \infty} u_n = 0$.

Proof. It is easy to verify that $u_n = s_n - s_{n-1}$. If n is large and if the series $\sum_0^\infty u_k$ is convergent, then s_{n-1} and s_n are both close to s (the sum of the series), and therefore u_n must be close to $s - s = 0$.

Stated in words this says that if a series converges, the nth term must approach zero as n approaches infinity.

COROLLARY 3e. If $\lim_{n \to \infty} u_n = 0$ fails to hold, the series $\sum_0^\infty u_k$ diverges.

For example, we see that the series

$$\sum_0^\infty \frac{(-1)^k k}{k+4}$$

is divergent because $\lim_{k \to \infty} [(-1)^k k/(k+4)] = 0$ is not true. The reader must, however, beware of assuming that if the nth term of a series approaches zero, the series converges. It may or may not. We shall show in the next section that the series

$$\sum_1^\infty \frac{1}{n}$$

is divergent even though here the relation $\lim_{n \to \infty} (1/n) = 0$ holds true.

PROBLEMS

1. If $\sum_{n=1}^\infty n^{-2} = \pi^2/6$, find $\sum_{n=5}^\infty n^{-2}$ correct to three decimal places.

2. It can be shown that the series

$$\sum_1^\infty \frac{1}{n^5} = s$$

is convergent. It can also be shown that if

$$R_{10} = \sum_{11}^\infty \frac{1}{n^5},$$

then $0 \leq R_{10} \leq 0.000025$. Use this fact to find s correct to within an error not exceeding one unit in the fourth decimal place.

3. Does the series

$$\sum_{n=3} \sin\left(\frac{\pi n}{3}\right)$$

converge? Justify your answer. The same question for

$$\sum_{n=1}^{\infty} \sin(\pi n).$$

4. Find the sum of the series

$$\sum_{n=0}^{\infty} (2^{-n} + 3^{-n}).$$

Evaluate the following repeating decimals. The answer should be a rational number.

5. $1.7313131 \cdots$.

6. $.42165165165 \cdots$.

7. $2.134444 \cdots$.

4. Integral Test

This section is devoted to the development of a very powerful method of testing whether certain series converge. All the series which we shall discuss in this section through Sec. 6 have nonnegative terms. Beginning in Sec. 7 we shall discuss series with terms of mixed sign.

We require the following fact about the real number system \Re which we assume without proof. The statement below is a slightly abbreviated form of Axiom 1a of the Appendix.

Let $s_n (n = 0, 1, 2, \cdots)$ be an infinite sequence which is nondecreasing, $s_0 \leq s_1 \leq s_2 \leq \cdots$. Then either $\lim_{n\to\infty} s_n$ exists, or the s_n's increase without limit as $n \to \infty$; that is, given any number M, there is an index n_0 such that $s_n \geq M$ if $n \geq n_0$. In this case we write $\lim_{n\to\infty} s_n = \infty$; such a sequence is divergent, but in a special way.

THEOREM 4a. Let $f(x)$ be a positive nonincreasing function for $N \leq x < \infty$. If

$$\int_{N}^{\infty} f(x)\, dx = \lim_{k\to\infty} \int_{N}^{k} f(x)\, dx = S < \infty$$

then the series $\displaystyle\sum_{N+1}^{\infty} f(n) = s$ where $s \leq S$.

If

$$\int_{N+1}^{\infty} f(x)\, dx = \lim_{k\to\infty} \int_{N+1}^{k} f(x)\, dx = \infty$$

then $\displaystyle\sum_{N+1}^{\infty} f(n) = \infty.$

Proof. Since $f(x)$ is positive and nonincreasing, we see by comparing areas (Fig. 1) that

$$f(n) \le \int_{n-1}^{n} f(x)\, dx .$$

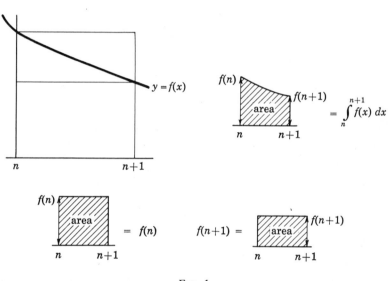

Fig. 1

It follows that

$$s_n = f(N+1) + \cdots + f(n)$$

$$\le \int_{N}^{N+1} f(x)\, dx + \cdots + \int_{n-1}^{n} f(x)\, dx$$

$$\le \int_{N}^{n} f(x)\, dx .$$

Since $(s_n)_N^{\infty}$ is nondecreasing (why?), it follows from the assumption made at the beginning of this section that $\lim_{n\to\infty} s_n = s$ exists and evidently $s \le S$.

On the other hand $\qquad f(n) \ge \displaystyle\int_{n}^{n+1} f(x)\, dx .$

Thus

$$s_n = f(N+1) + \cdots + f(n)$$

$$\geq \int_{N+1}^{N+2} f(x)\,dx + \cdots + \int_{n}^{n+1} f(x)\,dx$$

$$\geq \int_{N+1}^{n+1} f(x)\,dx \, .$$

If $\int_{N+1}^{n+1} f(x)\,dx$ increases beyond all bounds as $n \to \infty$, so must s_n.

It is important to note that instead of $\int_{N}^{\infty} f(x)\,dx$, we can consider $\int_{M}^{\infty} f(x)\,dx$ where M is *any* convenient lower limit. This is essentially because of Theorem 3c. If $f(x)$ is infinite at $x = 0$, one should always choose an $M > 0$.

The series

(1) $$\sum_{1}^{\infty} \frac{1}{n} = 1 + \frac{1}{2} + \frac{1}{3} + \frac{1}{4} + \cdots$$

is called the harmonic series. Since $1/n = f(n)$ where $f(x) = 1/x$ and since $1/x$ is positive and decreasing, the integral test applies. We have

$$\int_{1}^{k} \frac{1}{x}\,dx = (\log x)_{1}^{k} = \log k \, .$$

Since this increases beyond all bounds as $k \to \infty$, the integral test shows that the series **(1)** is divergent.

On the other hand consider the series

(2) $$\sum_{1}^{\infty} \frac{1}{n^2} = 1 + \frac{1}{4} + \frac{1}{9} + \frac{1}{16} + \cdots$$

Here $1/n^2 = f(n)$ where $f(x) = 1/x^2$. Since $f(x)$ is positive and decreasing, the integral test applies. We have

$$\int_{1}^{k} \frac{dx}{x^2} = \left[-\frac{1}{x} \right]_{1}^{k} = 1 - \frac{1}{k}$$

so that

$$\int_{1}^{\infty} \frac{dx}{x^2} = 1 \, .$$

It follows that the series **(2)** converges (and also that $\sum_{2}^{\infty} 1/n^2 \leq 1$ and hence $\sum_{1}^{\infty} 1/n^2 \leq 2$).

PROBLEMS

Using the integral test determine which of the following series are convergent and which divergent.

1. $\displaystyle\sum_{n=1}^{\infty} \frac{1}{n^3}$.

2. $\displaystyle\sum_{n=1}^{\infty} \frac{1}{\sqrt{n}}$.

3. $\displaystyle\sum_{n=0}^{\infty} ne^{-n^2}$.

4. $\displaystyle\sum_{n=0}^{\infty} \frac{n^4}{2n^5 + 3}$.

5. $\displaystyle\sum_{1}^{\infty} \frac{1}{(3n)^{5/4}}$.

6. $\displaystyle\sum_{1}^{\infty} \frac{\log n}{n}$.

7. $\displaystyle\sum_{2}^{\infty} \frac{1}{n(\log n)}$.

8. $\displaystyle\sum_{2}^{\infty} \frac{1}{n(\log n)^2}$.

9. Show that the series $\displaystyle\sum_{1}^{\infty} n^{-\lambda}$ is convergent if $\lambda > 1$.

10. Show that the series $\displaystyle\sum_{1}^{\infty} n^{-\lambda}$ is divergent if $0 < \lambda \leq 1$. HINT: It is convenient to treat the cases $\lambda = 1$ and $0 < \lambda < 1$ separately. What happens if $\lambda \leq 0$?

11. Show that the series $\displaystyle\sum_{2}^{\infty} n^{-1} (\log n)^{-\nu}$ is convergent if $\nu > 1$ and divergent if $\nu \leq 1$.

4*. Error Estimates

Suppose we have a convergent series $\sum_1^\infty u_n = s$. Then we know that $S_N = \sum_1^N u_n$ will be "close to" s if N is large. A question of great practical importance is "how close" is S_N to s. Since

$$s = S_N + R_N \qquad \text{where } R_N = \sum_{N+1}^\infty u_n$$

the problem reduces to estimating the remainder R_N. Of course this estimation cannot be made without further assumptions. Suppose that in point of fact the conditions of Theorem 4a are satisfied; that is, $u_n = f(n)$ where $f(x)$ is a positive decreasing function. Then by the arguments of Sec. 4.

(1) $$0 \le R_N = \sum_{N+1}^\infty u_n \le \int_N^\infty f(x)\, dx .$$

The expression $\int_N^\infty f(x)\, dx$ is thus a *majorant* for R_N.

EXAMPLE 1. Estimate the degree of approximation of $s = \sum_1^\infty n^{-2}$ by s_6. We have $u_n = n^{-2}$. (See Table 1.)

Table 1

u_1	1.000
u_2	0.250
u_3	0.111
u_4	0.063
u_5	0.040
u_6	0.028
s_6	1.492

By (1) $$R_6 = \sum_7^\infty n^{-2} \le \int_6^\infty \frac{dx}{x^2} = \left[-\frac{1}{x} \right]_6^\infty = \frac{1}{6} \le 0.17 .$$

Thus $$s = 1.49 \pm 0.17 .$$

This notation means that

$$| s - 1.49 | \le 0.17 .$$

It can be shown by advanced methods that

$$\sum_1^\infty n^{-2} = \frac{\pi^2}{6} = 1.65 \cdots ,$$

which is an agreement with our computations.

Frequently one wishes to compute the sum of a series $s = \sum_1^\infty u_n$ to specified degree of accuracy. For example, one might wish to compute s to three decimal places with an error of at most one unit in the third place. To do this, we must choose N so large that the remainder $R_N = \sum_{N+1}^\infty u_n$ does not exceed in absolute value 0.0005. If N is so chosen and if we compute S_N using four decimal places (or five decimal places if N is large) and round off the result to three places, the number obtained will give s to the prescribed degree of accuracy.

EXAMPLE 2. Compute $s = \sum_1^\infty 1/n^4$ to three decimal places with an error of not more than one unit in the third place. We have

$$0 \le R_N = \sum_{N+1}^\infty \frac{1}{n^4} \le \int_N^\infty x^{-4}\, dx = \frac{1}{3N^3},$$

and this is less than 0.0005 if $N = 9$. Thus if we compute

$$\frac{1}{1^4} + \frac{1}{2^4} + \cdots + \frac{1}{9^4} = 1.0821 \cdots$$

and round off three places, we can be sure that

$$s = 1.082 \pm 0.001 .$$

Now it is known that $\sum_1^\infty n^{-4} = \pi^4/90 = 1.082 \cdots$, as we should expect.

PROBLEMS

1. (a) How many terms of the series $\sum_1^\infty 1/n^2$ are needed to compute the sum correct to two decimal places with an error of at most one unit in the second place?

(b) How many terms of the series $\sum_1^\infty 1/n^2$ are needed to compute the sum correct to three decimal places with an error of at most one unit in the third place? (Do not compute the sums of these series.)

2. (a) How many terms of the series $\sum_1^\infty n^{-3/2}$ are needed to compute the sum correct to four decimal places with an error of at most one unit in the fourth place?

(b) How many terms of the series $\sum_1^\infty n^{-5/2}$ are needed to compute the sum correct to four decimal places with an error of at most one unit in the fourth place? (Do not compute the sums of these series.)

In the following exercises first find the smallest value of N such that S_N can be used to compute s to the required degree of accuracy. Compute S_N using one or two more decimal places than required. Finally round off to the specified number of decimal places.

3. Compute $\sum_1^\infty 1/n^3$ correct to two decimal places with an error of at most one unit in the second place.

4. Compute $\sum_1^\infty n/(n^2 + 4)^4$ correct to three decimal places with an error of at most one unit in the third place.

5. Compute $\sum_1^\infty ne^{-n^2}$ correct to four decimal places with an error of at most one unit in the fourth place. (In order to work this problem a table of exponentials is needed.)

5. Comparison Test

Powerful as the integral test is, it is not always convenient to apply it. For example, consider the series

$$(1) \qquad \sum_1^\infty \frac{n^2 - n}{n^4 + 2} \quad \text{and} \quad \sum_1^\infty \frac{n^3 + 1}{n^4 + 2}.$$

We can in principle determine whether these series converge or diverge by examining

$$(2) \qquad \int_1^k \frac{x^2 - x}{x^4 + 2}\, dx \quad \text{and} \quad \int_1^k \frac{x^3 + 1}{x^4 + 2}\, dx;$$

however, it is far from easy (although it is possible!) to carry out the necessary integrations. Among other applications the *comparison tests* make it unnecessary to integrate expressions such as **(2)**.

THEOREM 5a. If

1. $0 \leq v_n \leq u_n \quad (n = 0, 1, 2, \cdots)$,

2. $\sum_0^\infty u_n$ converges,

then $\sum_0^\infty v_n$ converges.

Proof. Let $\sum_0^\infty u_n = s$. Then clearly if $t_n = v_0 + \cdots + v_n$ is the partial sum of index n of the series $\sum_0^\infty v_n$, we have

$$t_n \leq t_{n+1} \qquad (n = 0, 1, \cdots).$$

Because of Assumption 1,

$$t_n = \sum_{k=0}^n v_k \leq \sum_0^n u_k \leq \sum_0^\infty u_n = s \qquad (n = 0, 1, \cdots).$$

Applying Axiom 1a of the Appendix we obtain our desired result.

THEOREM 5b. If

1. $0 \leq u_n \leq v_n \quad (n = 0, 1, 2, \cdots)$,

2. $\sum_0^\infty u_n$ diverges,

then $\sum_0^\infty v_n$ diverges.

Proof. If $\sum_0^\infty v_n$ were to converge, then by Theorem 5a so would $\sum_0^\infty u_n$. Since we have assumed the contrary, the only possibility is that $\sum_0^\infty v_n$ diverges.

Note that as a result of Theorem 3a it is enough in Theorem 5a to have $0 \leq v_n \leq u_n$ for all *sufficiently* large n. Consider the first of the series in (1). Since

$$0 \leq \frac{n^2 - n}{n^4 + 2} \leq \frac{1}{n^2} \qquad (n \geq 1)$$

and since the integral test shows that $\sum_1^\infty 1/n^2$ converges, we see by Theorem 5a that

$$\sum_1^\infty \frac{n^2 - n}{n^4 + 2} \qquad \text{converges.}$$

Similarly
$$0 \leq \frac{1}{n} \leq \frac{n^3 + 1}{n^4 + 2} \qquad (n \geq 2),$$

and since the integral test shows that $\sum_1^\infty 1/n$ diverges, we see by Theorem 5b that

$$\sum \frac{n^3 + 1}{n^4 + 2} \qquad \text{diverges.}$$

The following result, which is a corollary of Theorem 5a and 5b, is very useful in practice.

THEOREM 5c. If $0 < u_n, 0 < v_n \ (n = 0, 1, \cdots)$ and if $\lim_{n \to \infty} (v_n/u_n) = t$ exists, $0 \leq t \leq \infty$, then:

1. if $0 < t < \infty$, the series $\sum_0^\infty v_n$ converges if $\sum_0^\infty u_n$ converges and diverges if $\sum_0^\infty u_n$ diverges;

2. if $t = 0$, the series $\sum_0^\infty v_n$ converges if $\sum_0^\infty u_n$ converges;

3. if $t = \infty$, the series $\sum_0^\infty v_n$ diverges if $\sum_0^\infty u_n$ diverges.[1]

Proof. Suppose that $0 < t < \infty$ and that $\sum_0^\infty u_n$ is convergent. Choose any number T larger than t. Then if N is "sufficiently large," v_n/u_n will be so close to t for $n \geq N$ that we shall have $v_n \leq Tu_n$ for $n \geq N$. We can now apply Theorem 5a and Theorem 3a. The other cases can be dealt with similarly.

EXAMPLE 1. Consider the series

(3)
$$\sum_0^\infty \frac{2n - 9}{n^4 + 2n^3 + 7n + 11}.$$

Here
$$v_n = \frac{2n - 9}{n^4 + 2n^3 + 7n + 11}.$$

[1] Although "∞" is not a number, it is nevertheless convenient to use $\lim_{n \to \infty} c_n = \infty$ to mean that c_n's grow beyond all bound as n increases to ∞; that is, given any (large) number T, there is an integer n_0 such that $c_n \geq T$ if $n \geq n_0$.

The question is how shall we choose u_n so as to be able to use the theory developed above. Note that if n is large, the percentage difference between $2n - 9$ and $2n$ is very small and also the percentage difference between $n^4 + 2_n^3 + 7n + 11$ and n^4 is very small. Thus for large n, v_n is not very different from $2n/n^4 = 2/n^3$. We therefore take

$$u_n = \frac{1}{n^3} .$$

Then

$$\frac{v_n}{u_n} = \frac{2n - 9}{n^4 + 2n^3 + 7n + 11} \cdot \frac{n^3}{1} .$$

Dividing numerator and denominator by n^4, we find that

$$\frac{v_n}{u_n} = \frac{2 - 9/n}{1 + 2/n + 7/n^2 + 11/n^4} ,$$

from which it is evident that

$$\lim_{n \to \infty} \frac{v_n}{u_n} = 2 .$$

An easy application of the integral test shows that $\Sigma_1^\infty \, 1/n^3$ converges, and thus by Part 1 of Theorem 5c the series (3) converges.

For rapidly convergent series it is often useful to use the comparison test with a geometric series as the test series.

LEMMA 5d. If u_n $(n = N, N + 1, N + 2, \cdots)$ is a sequence of nonnegative numbers and if for some number $r > 0$ we have

$$u_{n+1} \leqq r u_n \qquad (n = N, N + 1, \cdots),$$

then

$$u_{N+k} \leqq r^k u_N \qquad (k = 0, 1, 2, \cdots).$$

Proof. By assumption

$$u_{N+1} \leqq r u_N ,$$

$$u_{N+2} \leqq r u_{N+1} \leqq r(r u_N) = r^2 u_N ,$$

$$u_{N+3} \leqq r u_{N+2} \leqq r(r^2 u_N) = r^3 u_N, \text{ etc.}$$

THEOREM 5e. (The ratio test.) If $0 < u_n$ $(n = 0, 1, \cdots)$ and if the limit

$$\lim_{n \to \infty} \frac{u_{n+1}}{u_n} = R$$

exists, then the series $\Sigma_0^\infty \, u_n$:

1. converges if $0 \leqq R < 1$;
2. diverges if $\qquad R > 1$.

Note that if the limit in question does not exist or if it exists and is 1, the ratio test gives no information, and some other method must be used.

Proof. Suppose first that $0 < R < 1$. Choose any number r $(R < r < 1)$. Since $\lim_{n \to \infty} (u_{n+1}/u_n) = R$, it follows that if N is "sufficiently large," we shall have $u_{n+1}/u_n \leqq r$ $(n = N, N + 1, \cdots)$. By Lemma 5d this implies that $u_{N+k} \leqq r^k u_N$ for $k = 0, 1, \cdots$. The series $\sum_{k=0}^{\infty} r^k u_N$ converges by Theorem 2c. Applying the comparison test, Theorem 5a, we see that the series $\sum_{0}^{\infty} u_n$ converges.

We next turn to the case $R > 1$. If N is "sufficiently large," we shall have $u_{n+1} \geqq u_n (n = N, N + 1, \cdots)$. This says that from the term of index N on the successive terms of our series either remain the same or increase. Now apply Corollary 3e.

EXAMPLE 2. Apply the ratio test to the series

$$\sum_{n=0}^{\infty} \frac{1}{n!} .$$

Here $u_n = 1/n!$, so that

$$\frac{u_{n+1}}{u_n} = \frac{n!}{(n + 1)!} = \frac{1}{n + 1} .$$

It follows that

$$\lim_{n \to \infty} \frac{u_{n+1}}{u_n} = 0 .$$

Thus our series is convergent.

EXAMPLE 3. Apply the ratio test to the series

$$\sum_{1}^{\infty} \frac{1}{n^2} .$$

Here $u_n = 1/n^2$, and thus

$$\frac{u_{n+1}}{u_n} = \frac{n^2}{(n + 1)^2} = \frac{1}{1 + 2/n + 1/n^2} .$$

from which it follows that

$$\lim_{n \to \infty} \frac{u_{n+1}}{u_n} = 1 .$$

In this case we cannot conclude from the ratio test anything at all about our series. However we know from Sec. 4 (the integral test) that our series does converge.

PROBLEMS

Determine whether each of the following series is convergent or divergent. In each case give in full the argument on which you base your answer.

1. $\displaystyle\sum_{2}^{\infty} \frac{n^3 + 4n}{n^4 - 8}$.

2. $\displaystyle\sum_{0}^{\infty} \frac{n^2 - 1}{(n^2 + 1)^2}$.

3. $\displaystyle\frac{1}{1\cdot2\cdot3} + \frac{1}{2\cdot3\cdot4} + \frac{1}{3\cdot4\cdot5} + \cdots$.

4. $\displaystyle\sum_{0}^{\infty} \frac{1}{n^3 + 7}$.

5. $\displaystyle\sum_{0}^{\infty} \frac{1}{4n + 1}$.

6. $\displaystyle\sum_{2}^{\infty} \frac{1}{n^3 \log n}$.

7. $\displaystyle\sum_{1}^{\infty} \frac{\log n}{n + 2}$.

8. $\displaystyle\sum_{1}^{\infty} \frac{1}{n^2 + \log n}$.

9. $\displaystyle\sum_{1}^{\infty} \frac{1}{n \log (n^2 + 1)}$.

10. $\displaystyle\sum_{0}^{\infty} \frac{3^n}{n!}$.

11. $\displaystyle\sum_{0}^{\infty} \frac{n}{3^n}$.

12. $\displaystyle\sum_{0}^{\infty} \frac{(n!)^2}{(2n)!}$.

13. $\displaystyle\sum_{0}^{\infty} \frac{2^n}{3^n + n}$.

14. Write out a proof of Case 3 of Theorem 5c.

5*. Error Estimates Continued

In this section we shall consider the application of the comparison test to the problems of numerical computation.

Let $s = \Sigma_0^\infty v_n$ be a convergent series of nonnegative terms. To estimate the degree of approximation by $S_N = \Sigma_0^N v_n$, we must find an upper bound for $R_N = \Sigma_{N+1}^\infty v_n$. Clearly if $0 \leq v_n \leq u_n$ for $n = N+1, N+2, \cdots$, then $R_N \leq \Sigma_{N+1}^\infty u_n$. The choice of the u_n's is governed by two conditions: first the u_n's should be such that $\Sigma_{N+1}^\infty u_n$ is easily computed or majorized; second the u_n's must not be too much bigger than the v_n's, at least for n near $N+1$. If this second condition is not met, the computation may become needlessly laborious because N has been chosen larger than is necessary.

EXAMPLE 1. Estimate the degree of approximation of

$$s = \sum_2^\infty \frac{1}{n^3 \log n}$$

by the partial sum S_6. Here $v_n = 1/(n^3 \log n)$. If we set $u_n = 1/(n^3 \log 7)$, then clearly $0 \leq v_n \leq u_n$ for $n = 7, 8, \cdots$, and thus using the integral test majoration,

$$R_6 = \sum_7^\infty \frac{1}{n^3 \log n} \leq \sum_7^\infty \frac{1}{n^3 \log 7} \leq \frac{1}{\log 7} \int_6^\infty \frac{dx}{x^3}$$

$$= \frac{1}{2(\log 7)\, 6^2} = 0.0071 \cdots .$$

Routine computation gives $S_6 = 0.2331 \cdots$. Thus $s = 0.233 \pm 0.007$.

EXAMPLE 2. Estimate the degree of approximation of

$$e = \sum_0^\infty \frac{1}{n!}$$

by the partial sum of index 6. We must majorize $\Sigma_7^\infty v_n$ where $v_n = 1/n!$. We have

$$\frac{v_{n+1}}{v_n} = \frac{1}{n+1} \leq \frac{1}{8} \qquad \text{if } n \geq 7 .$$

By Lemma 5d $\qquad v_{7+k} \leq \frac{1}{7!} \left(\frac{1}{8}\right)^k \qquad (k = 0, 1, \cdots) .$

Thus $\qquad R_6 = \sum_{n=7}^\infty v_n \leq \sum_{k=0}^\infty \frac{1}{7!} \left(\frac{1}{8}\right)^k = \frac{1}{7!} \cdot \frac{8}{7} = 0.00023 .$

Here we have used the formula for the sum of a geometric series instead of the integral test majoration. Computing S_6, we find that

$$e = 2.7180 \pm 0.0003 .$$

PROBLEMS

1. Compute $\sum_{2}^{\infty} (2/n(n-1))^{5/2}$ correct to two decimal places with an error of not more than one unit in the second place. Answer: 1.08 ± 0.01.

2. Compute $\sum_{1}^{\infty} 1/n(n+1)(n+2)(n+3)$ correct to three decimal places with an error of not more than one unit in the third place.

3. Compute $\sum_{2}^{\infty} 1/n^3(\log n)^2$ correct to two decimal places with an error of not more than one unit in the third place.

4. Compute $\sum_{1}^{\infty} 1/n^n$ correct to three decimal places with an error of not more than one unit in the third place. Answer: 1.291 ± 0.001.

5. Compute $\sum_{1}^{\infty} 5/n2^n$ to three decimal places with an error of not more than one unit in the third place.

6. Compute $\sum_{0}^{\infty} (1/n!)^2$ to three decimal places with an error of not more than one unit in the third place.

7. Compute $\sum_{0}^{\infty} (n+1)3^{-n}$ to four decimal places with an error of not more than one unit in the fourth place.

6. Relative Magnitudes

The present section is devoted to proving that for example, $\lim_{n \to \infty} n^{98}(5/4)^{-n} = 0$. Expressed (less precisely) in words this relation says that for n "sufficiently large" n^{98} is very much smaller than $(5/4)^n$. Many problems in series depend essentially upon recognizing such relations.

LEMMA 6a. If c is a real number greater than 1 and if m is any real number, then

$$(1) \qquad\qquad \lim_{n \to \infty} \frac{n^m}{c^n} = 0 \,.$$

Proof. We may restrict ourselves to the case where $m > 0$ since if $m \leq 0$, our conclusion is obvious. Instead of **(1)** we shall prove the (slightly) stronger result[1] $\lim_{x \to \infty} (x^m/c^x) = 0$. Since $x^m/c^x = (x/e^{rx})^m$ where $r = (1/m) \log_e c > 0$, if we can prove that $\lim_{x \to \infty} (x/e^{rx}) = 0$ for $r > 0$, our desired result will follow. A familiar elementary result of L'Hospital asserts that if we have two functions $f(x)$ and $g(x)$ both increasing to $+\infty$ as x increases to $+\infty$ and if $\lim_{x \to \infty} [f'(x)/g'(x)]$ exists, then $\lim_{x \to \infty} [f(x)/g(x)]$ exists and the two limits are equal. Let us apply this result to $f(x) = x$ and $g(x) = e^{rx}$. We have

$$\lim_{x \to \infty} \frac{f'(x)}{g'(x)} = \lim_{x \to \infty} \frac{1}{re^{rx}} = 0$$

and consequently $\qquad \lim_{x \to \infty} \frac{f(x)}{g(x)} = \lim_{x \to \infty} \frac{x}{e^{rx}} = 0 \,.$

[1] By $x \to \infty$ we mean here $x \to +\infty$.

LEMMA 6b. If b is any positive real number and if m is any real number, then

$$\lim_{n \to \infty} \frac{(\log n)^m}{n^b} = 0 .$$

Proof. Again we may assume m positive. If $c = b/m$, then

$$\frac{(\log x)^m}{x^b} = \left(\frac{\log x}{x^c} \right)^m$$

where $c > 0$. It is therefore enough to show that if $c > 0$,

$$\lim_{n \to \infty} \frac{\log x}{x^c} = 0 .$$

This follows by an application of L'Hôpital's theorem, see Problem 1.

EXAMPLE 1. Discuss the convergence of the series

(2) $$\sum_{1}^{\infty} \frac{n^2 + 1}{2^{-n} n^4 + n^3} .$$

We wish of course to apply a comparison test. Here $v_n = (n^2 + 1)/(2^{-n} n^4 + n^3)$. It is necessary to guess a suitable u_n. Proceeding rather informally, we note that Lemma 6a tells us that $2^{-n} n^4$ is "very small indeed." Thus we would expect v_n to be more or less the same size as n^2/n^3; consequently we choose $u_n = 1/n$. We have

$$\frac{v_n}{u_n} = \frac{n^2 + 1}{2^{-n} n^4 + n^3} \cdot \frac{n}{1} .$$

Dividing the numerator and denominator by n^3 yields

$$\frac{v_n}{u_n} = \frac{1 + 1/n^2}{2^{-n} n + 1} .$$

Using Lemma 6a (this time rigorously), we see that

$$\lim_{n \to \infty} \frac{v_n}{u_n} = \frac{1}{1} = 1 .$$

The series $\sum_{1}^{\infty} 1/n$ diverges, and thus by Theorem 5c so does the series (2).

EXAMPLE 2. Discuss the convergence of the series

(3) $$\sum_{1}^{\infty} \frac{(\log n)^3}{n^2} .$$

Here $v_n = (\log n)^3/n^2$. Although the formula for v_n is fairly simple, the integral

test is not convenient because the integration involved is difficult. Again we first proceed rather informally. Lemma 6b asserts that $(\log n)^3$ is ultimately smaller than n^ϵ for any positive ϵ. Thus v_n is more or less the same size as $1/n^2$, so that the series (3) probably converges. However we cannot take $u_n = n^2$ (why not?); instead we take $u_n = n^{-3/2}$.

Then
$$\frac{v_n}{u_n} = \frac{(\log n)^3}{n^2} \cdot \frac{n^{3/2}}{1} = \frac{(\log n)^3}{n^{1/2}}.$$

By Lemma 6b
$$\lim_{n \to \infty} \frac{v_n}{u_n} = 0.$$

An easy application of the integral test shows that $\sum_1^\infty n^{-3/2}$ converges. By Theorem 5c so does the series (3). Note we could just as well have taken $u_n = n^{-c}$ for any c $(1 < c < 2)$.

PROBLEMS

1. Complete the proof of Lemma 6b.

Determine whether each of the following series is convergent or divergent. In each case give in full the arguments on which your answer is based.

2. $\displaystyle\sum_0^\infty \frac{n^2 \, 2^n}{3^n}.$

3. $\displaystyle\sum_1^\infty \frac{n \log n}{(n^2 + 1)^2}.$

4. $\displaystyle\sum_1^\infty \frac{\log n}{n + 2^n}.$

5. $\displaystyle\sum_1^\infty \frac{2^n}{(2^n + n)\, n}.$

6. $\displaystyle\sum_3^\infty \frac{\log \log n}{n^2}.$

7. $\displaystyle\sum_3^\infty \frac{\log n}{n(\log \log n)^2}.$

8. $\displaystyle\sum_1^\infty \frac{(\log n)^2}{n!}.$

7. Absolute Convergence

So far we have worked only with series which have positive terms. We are now going to deal with series in which the terms are of mixed sign.

DEFINITION 7a. The series $\sum_0^\infty u_n$ is said to converge absolutely if the series $\sum_0^\infty |u_n|$ converges.

Consider the series

$$\text{(1)} \qquad \sum_1^\infty \frac{(-1)^n}{n^2}.$$

To see if this series converges absolutely, we look at the series

$$\text{(2)} \qquad \sum_1^\infty \frac{1}{n^2}.$$

Since it converges, the series (1) does converge absolutely. It may be objected that the statement that the series (1) converges absolutely is really a statement about the series (2) and tells us nothing about the convergence or divergence of (1). This objection is met by the following theorem.

THEOREM 7b. If the series $\sum_0^\infty u_n$ converges absolutely, it converges.

Proof. By assumption the series

$$\text{(2)} \qquad \sum_0^\infty |u_n|$$

converges. We have

$$0 \leq \tfrac{1}{2}(u_n + |u_n|) \leq |u_n| \qquad (n = 0, 1, \cdots),$$

and therefore by Theorem 5a we see that

$$\text{(3)} \qquad \sum_0^\infty \tfrac{1}{2}(u_n + |u_n|) \qquad \text{converges.}$$

Similarly $\qquad 0 \leq \tfrac{1}{2}(-u_n + |u_n|) \leq |u_n| \qquad (n = 0, 1, \cdots),$

and therefore by Theorem 5a

$$\text{(4)} \qquad \sum_0^\infty \tfrac{1}{2}(-u_n + |u_n|) \qquad \text{converges.}$$

Since $\qquad u_n = \tfrac{1}{2}(u_n + |u_n|) - \tfrac{1}{2}(-u_n + |n_n|),$

Theorems 3a and 3b imply that $\sum_0^\infty u_n$ converges.

The reader should note that

$$\tfrac{1}{2}(u_n + |u_n|) = \begin{cases} u_n & \text{if } u_n > 0 \\ 0 & \text{if } u_n \leq 0 \end{cases}$$

and thus the series (**3**) is the series composed of just the positive terms from $\Sigma_0^\infty u_n$, the remaining terms having been replaced by zeros. Similarly

$$\tfrac{1}{2}(-u_n + |u_n|) = \begin{cases} -u_n & \text{if } u_n < 0 \\ 0 & \text{if } u_n \geq 0 \end{cases},$$

and thus the series (**4**) is the series composed of minus the negative terms from $\Sigma_0^\infty u_n$, the remaining terms having been replaced by zeros. We leave to the reader to prove that conversely in a series of mixed terms if the series made from the positive terms (the remaining terms replaced by zeros) converges and if the series made from minus the negative terms (the remaining, etc.) converges, the original series converges absolutely.

Consider the series

(**5**)
$$\sum_1^\infty \frac{(-1)^{n-1}}{n}.$$

Since the series

$$\sum_1^\infty \frac{1}{n}$$

diverges, the series (**5**) does not converge absolutely. Note that this does not prove that it does not converge.

DEFINITION 7a. A series which converges but does not converge absolutely is said to converge *conditionally*.

In the next section we shall show that the series (**5**) is convergent, and therefore since it is not absolutely convergent, it is conditionally convergent.

8. Alternating Series

An alternating series is one in which the terms are alternately positive and negative, that is, one of the form

(**1**)
$$\sum_0^\infty (-1)^n a_n \quad \text{where } a_n \geq 0, \quad n = 0, 1, \cdots.$$

Note that the term of index n of this series is not a_n but $(-1)^n a_n$.

THEOREM 8a. If

 1. $a_n \geqq a_{n+1}$ $(n = 0, 1, \cdots)$,

 2. $\lim\limits_{n \to \infty} a_n = 0$,

then the series (1) converges.

Proof. To see this, mark down the partial sums S_0, S_1, S_2, \cdots, on the real axis. Since $S_1 = S_0 - a_1$, we see that S_1 lies to the left of S_0. Next since $S_2 = S_1 + a_2$, S_2 lies to the right of S_1, but since $S_2 = S_0 - a_1 + a_2$ and since, by Assumption 1, $a_1 \geqq a_2$, S_2 lies to the left of S_0. Again since $S_3 = S_2 - a_3$, S_3 lies to the left of S_2, but since $S_3 = S_1 + a_2 - a_3$ and since $a_2 \geqq a_3$, S_3 lies to the right of S_1. (See Fig. 2).

FIG. 2

Clearly we can continue this argument, and we see that S_n always lies between S_{n-1} and S_{n-2}. Consider the odd partial sums S_1, S_3, S_5, \cdots. These are increasing, and they are all bounded above by S_0. Thus by Axiom 1a of the Appendix, $\lim\limits_{n \to \infty} S_{2n+1}$ exists. Call this limit S. Since $S_{2n} = S_{2n+1} + a_{2n+1}$, we have, using Assumption 2, $\lim\limits_{n \to \infty} S_{2n} = S$. Thus $\lim\limits_{n \to \infty} S_n = S$, and our theorem is proved.

Consider the series

(2)
$$\sum_1^\infty \frac{(-1)^n}{n}.$$

The assumptions of Theorem 8a are satisfied, and thus the series (2) converges. We proved in Sec. 7 that the series (2) does not converge absolutely. Therefore by definition it converges conditionally.

Since S lies between S_n and S_{n+1} for every n, we see that S_n differs from S (the sum of the series) by less than a_{n+1}, the distance between S_n and S_{n+1}, and that if the first term neglected, $(-1)^{n+1} a_{n+1}$, is positive, then S is somewhat greater than S_n whereas if the first term neglected is negative, then S is somewhat less than S_n. These facts are of great importance in computations.

EXAMPLE 1. Consider the series

$$\sum_1^\infty \frac{(-1)^{n-1}}{n^4}.$$

If we wish to compute the sum of this series correct to three decimal places with an error of at most one unit in the third place, then by the discussion given after the proof of Theorem 8a it will be enough to choose N so large that

$$u_{N+1} = (N+1)^{-4} \leqq 0.0005.$$

This inequality is verified if $N + 1 = 7$. Thus if we compute

$$\frac{1}{1^4} - \frac{1}{2^4} + \frac{1}{3^4} - \frac{1}{4^4} + \frac{1}{5^4} - \frac{1}{6^4} = 0.9467 \cdots$$

and round off to three places, we can be sure that

(3) $$\sum_1^\infty \frac{(-1)^{n-1}}{n^4} = 0.947 \pm 0.001 .$$

Now it is known that

$$\sum_1^\infty \frac{(-1)^{n-1}}{n^4} = \frac{7\pi^4}{720},$$

from which one can obtain an independent check of the correctness of (3).

PROBLEMS

Determine whether each of the following series is conditionally convergent, absolutely convergent, or divergent. In each case give in full the arguments on which your answer is based.

1. $$\sum_1^\infty \frac{(-1)^n}{\sqrt{n}} .$$

2. $$\sum_1^\infty (-1)^n \sqrt{n} .$$

3. $$\sum_1^\infty \frac{(-1)^n}{n^3} .$$

4. $$\sum_1^\infty \frac{(-1)^n n}{2^n} .$$

5. $$\sum_1^\infty \frac{(-1)^n n}{\log n} .$$

6. $$\sum_2^\infty \frac{(-1)^n}{\log n} .$$

7. $$1 + \frac{1}{2^1} - \frac{1}{2^2} - \frac{1}{2^3} + \frac{1}{2^4} + \frac{1}{2^5} - \frac{1}{2^6} - \frac{1}{2^7} + \cdots .$$

8. $$\sum_1^\infty \frac{(-1)^{n+1} n}{(n^2 + 1)} .$$

9. $$\sum_0^\infty \frac{(-1)^n 5^n}{n!} .$$

10. $\displaystyle\sum_{1}^{\infty} \frac{(-1)^n \, 2^n}{(n^6 + 1)^2}$.

11. $\dfrac{1}{1^2} + \dfrac{1}{2^2} - \dfrac{1}{3^2} - \dfrac{1}{4^2} + \dfrac{1}{5^2} + \cdots$.

12. Compute $\displaystyle\sum_{1}^{\infty} \frac{(-1)^n}{n2^n}$ correct to three decimal places with an error of at most one unit in the third place.

13. Compute $\displaystyle\sum_{0}^{\infty} \frac{(-1)^n}{n!}$ correct to four decimal places with an error of at most one unit in the fourth place.

14. Compute $\displaystyle\sum_{1}^{\infty} \frac{(-1)^n}{n^3}$ correct to two decimal places with an error of at most one unit in the second place.

15. Compute $\displaystyle\sum_{1}^{\infty} \frac{(-1)^n \, n}{2^n}$ correct to three decimal places with an error of at most one unit in the third place.

9. Power Series

In this section we shall apply all our earlier methods to the study of series of the form

(1) $$\sum_{0}^{\infty} b_n(x - c)^n .$$

A series of this form is called a power series. The value c is the *center* of the series. A power series is, of course, not one series but a family of series, one for each assignment of the variable x. Our objective is to determine for each value of x whether the series **(1)** converges absolutely, converges conditionally, or diverges. Consider, for example, the series

(2) $$\sum_{1}^{\infty} \frac{(x - 3)^n}{n^{1/2} \, 4^n} .$$

Here $u_n = (x - 3)^n/n^{1/2} \, 4^n$. We begin by applying the ratio test, Theorem 5e, to the series $\sum_{1}^{\infty} | u_n |$. We have

$$\left| \frac{u_{n+1}}{u_n} \right| = \left| \frac{(x - 3)^{n+1}}{(n + 1)^{1/2} \, 4^{n+1}} \cdot \frac{n^{1/2} \, 4^n}{(x - 3)^n} \right| = \frac{| (x - 3) |}{4(1 + 1/n)^{1/2}} .$$

It follows that

$$\lim_{n \to \infty} \left| \frac{u_{n+1}}{u_n} \right| = \frac{|(x-3)|}{4}.$$

By the ratio test the series (**2**) converges absolutely whenever

$$\frac{|(x-3)|}{4} < 1.$$

This is equivalent to

$$|x-3| < 4$$

which holds if x is less than four units from 3, that is, if $-1 < x < 7$. Thus the series (**2**) converges absolutely if $-1 < x < 7$. By the ratio test the series (**2**) diverges whenever

$$\frac{|x-3|}{4} > 1.$$

This is equivalent to

$$|x-3| > 4$$

which holds if x is more than four units from 3, that is, if $x < -1$ or $x > 7$. Thus for these values of x the series (**2**) diverges. It only remains to determine the behavior of the series for $x = -1$ and $x = 7$. For these values the ratio test gives no information. If we put $x = 7$ in (**2**), we obtain

$$\sum_{1}^{\infty} \frac{(7-3)^n}{n^{1/2}\, 4^n} = \sum_{1}^{\infty} \frac{1}{n^{1/2}}.$$

The integral test shows this series to be divergent. If we put $x = -1$ in (**2**), we obtain

$$\sum_{1}^{\infty} \frac{(-1-3)^n}{n^{1/2}\, 4^n} = \sum_{1}^{\infty} \frac{(-1)^n}{n^{1/2}}$$

which by Theorem 8a is conditionally convergent.

Our information can be conveniently summarized on a graph (Fig. 3).

It is to be noted that a power series always converges for at least one value, namely $x = c$ where c is the center of the series.

FIG. 3

PROBLEMS

For each power series given below determine the convergence properties of the series for all values of x.

1. $\displaystyle\sum_{1}^{\infty} \frac{1}{n} x^n$.

2. $\displaystyle\sum_{0}^{\infty} (x - 3)^n \, 2^n$.

3. $\displaystyle\sum_{0}^{\infty} \frac{(x - 2)^n}{n!}$.

4. $\displaystyle\sum_{0}^{\infty} x^n \, n!$.

5. $1 + \dfrac{x^2}{\sqrt{2}} + \dfrac{x^4}{\sqrt{4}} + \cdots$.

6. $x - \dfrac{x^3}{3!} + \dfrac{x^5}{5!} + \cdots$.

7. $\displaystyle\sum_{0}^{\infty} \frac{(x + \frac{1}{2})^n}{1 + n^2}$.

8. $\displaystyle\sum_{1}^{\infty} (x - 1)^n \frac{(-3)^n}{n}$.

9. $\displaystyle\sum_{0}^{\infty} \frac{(-1)^n \, x^{2n}}{(2n)!}$.

10. $1 + x + x^4 + x^9 + x^{16} + \cdots$.

11. $\displaystyle\sum_{1}^{\infty} \frac{x^n}{n^n}$.

12. $\displaystyle\sum_{3}^{\infty} \frac{(x - 5)^n}{2^n \, n(\log n)^2}$.

13. $\displaystyle\sum_{3}^{\infty} \frac{(x - 5)^n}{2^n \, n(\log n)}$.

14. $\displaystyle\sum_{0}^{\infty} \left(x - \frac{3}{2}\right)^n \left(\frac{2}{3}\right)^n n$.

15. $\displaystyle\sum_{0}^{\infty} n! \, x^{2n}$.

10. Additional Exercises

The following problems give two additional tests for convergence.

1. Let $u_1 \geq u_2 \geq u_3 \geq \cdots \geq 0$. Prove that the series $\sum_1^\infty u_n$ and the series $\sum_1^\infty 2^n u_{2^n}$ both converge or both diverge. HINT: Show that

$$\sum_{2^n+1}^{2^{n+1}} u_k \leq 2^n u_{2^n} \leq 2 \sum_{2^{n-1}+1}^{2^n} u_k.$$

This result is known as Cauchy's condensation test.

2. (a) Use Problem 1 and Theorem 2c to prove that

$$\sum_1^\infty n^{-\lambda}$$

converges if $\lambda > 1$ and diverges for $\lambda \leq 1$.

(b) Use Problem 1 and part a of this problem to prove that

$$\sum_2^\infty n^{-1} (\log n)^{-\nu}$$

converges if $\nu > 1$ and diverges for $\nu \leq 1$.

3. (a) Use the mean value theorem[1] to prove that if $\lambda > 0$, $c > 0$ and if $u_n = (n+c)^{-\lambda}$, then

$$\frac{u_{n+1}}{u_n} \geq 1 - \frac{\lambda}{n+c} \qquad (n = 0, 1, \cdots).$$

(b) Using this shows that if $(v_n)_0^\infty$ is a sequence with positive terms such that for some $\lambda > 0$ and $c > 0$

(1) $$\frac{v_{n+1}}{v_n} \leq 1 - \frac{\lambda}{n+c} \qquad (n = 0, 1, \cdots),$$

then

$$v_n \leq A(n+c)^{-\lambda} \qquad (n = 0, 1, \cdots).$$

(c) Deduce that if (**1**) holds and if $\lambda > 1$, then $\sum_0^\infty v_n$ is convergent.

(d) Develop a similar test for divergence.

[1] The mean value theorem asserts that if $f(x) \in \mathbb{C}^{(1)}$ for $a \leq x \leq b$, then for some ξ $(a < \xi < b)$ we have $f(b) - f(a) = f'(\xi)(b - a)$. Here $f(x) \in \mathbb{C}^{(1)}$ for $a \leq x \leq b$ means that $f(x)$ and $f'(x)$ are continuous for $a \leq x \leq b$.

4. Use the results of Problem 3 to discuss the convergence of the series

(**2**)
$$\sum_0^\infty \binom{\nu}{n} (-1)^n$$

for different values of ν. Here $\binom{\nu}{0} = 1$, and

$$\binom{\nu}{n} = \frac{\nu(\nu-1)\cdots(\nu-n+1)}{n!} \qquad \text{if } n \geq 1 .$$

Note that the terms of the series (**2**) will have the same sign for all sufficiently large n.

[2]

Taylor Series

1. Introduction

Suppose that we are given a function $f(x)$ and a number c. It is natural to wonder if it is possible to represent the function $f(x)$ as a power series with center c,

(1) $$f(x) = a_0 + a_1(x - c) + a_2(x - c)^2 + a_3(x - c)^3 + \cdots,$$

for all or at least for some values of x. It is of course clear that in order for the relation (1) to be valid, we must choose the constants a_0, a_1, a_2, \cdots, correctly— their choice depending upon the function $f(x)$ and upon c. Our problem is to discover what the correct choice is. Let us therefore *assume* that $f(x)$ has an expansion of the form (1). If we put $x = c$ in (1), all terms except the first are 0, and we find that

(2₀) $$f(c) = a_0;$$

thus we see at least how to choose the coefficient a_0. Let us now (for reasons which will be apparent in a moment) differentiate (1). Treating the infinite sum on the right-hand side of (1) as if it were a finite sum, that is, a polynomial, we obtain

$$f'(x) = a_1 + 2a_2(x - c) + 3a_3(x - c)^2 + 4a_4(x - c)^3 + \cdots.$$

If we put $x = c$ here, we find this time that

(2₁) $$f'(c) = a_1,$$

a formula for a_1. We now differentiate again to get

$$f''(x) = 2a_2 + 3.2a_3(x - c) + 4.3a_4(x - c)^2 + \cdots,$$

from which on setting $x = c$, we find that

(2₂) $$f''(c) = 2a_2 \quad \text{or} \quad \frac{1}{2!} f''(c) = a_2.$$

Further applications of this procedure give

(2_3) $$f'''(c) = 6a_3 \quad \text{or} \quad \frac{1}{3!} f'''(c) = a_3 ,$$

(2_4) $$f^{(4)}(c) = 24a_4 \quad \text{or} \quad \frac{1}{4!} f^{(4)}(c) = a_4 , \qquad \text{etc.}$$

From the special cases (2_0) through (2_4) the general formula

(3) $$a_n = \frac{1}{n!} f^{(n)}(c)$$

is apparent. The argument we have given is vague and depended at several points on doubtful procedures (for example, treating an infinite sum as if it were a finite one). Moreover we began by *assuming* that it was possible to expend $f(x)$ in a power series about the center c. Thus we have really *proved* nothing although our argument has been very *suggestive*.

DEFINITION 1a. Let $f(x)$ be infinitely differentiable in an interval including c in its interior. The series

(4) $$\sum_0^\infty \frac{f^{(n)}(c)}{n!} (x - c)^n$$

is called the Taylor series with center c generated by f.

Note that we cannot write

$$f(x) = \sum_0^\infty \frac{f^{(n)}(c)}{n!} (x - c)^n$$

since we have *not proved* that the series will converge for any values of x, nor have we proved that if it converges, it converges to $f(x)$. We therefore write

$$f(x) \sim \sum_0^\infty \frac{1}{n!} f^{(n)}(c) (x - c)^n .$$

It is evident from the discussion preceding Definition 1a that we *hope* the series (4) will converge to $f(x)$ for those values of x for which it converges. In Sec. 3 and 4 we shall prove that for *many common functions* the series (4) does in fact converge to $f(x)$ when it converges.

The most frequent choice for c is 0. In this case (4) reduces to

(5) $$\sum_0^\infty \frac{f^{(n)}(0)}{n!} x^n$$

which is called the Maclaurin series generated by $f(x)$. A Maclaurin series is thus just a Taylor series with center 0.

EXAMPLE 1. Let $f(x) = 1/(1-x)$ and $c = 0$. The coefficients neaded in **(5)** are most easily computed from a table such as the one below. We have

$$f(x) \quad = \frac{1}{1-x}, \qquad\qquad f(0) \quad = 1,$$

$$f'(x) \quad = \frac{1}{(1-x)^2}, \qquad\qquad f'(0) \quad = 1,$$

$$f^{(2)}(x) = \frac{2}{(1-x)^3}, \qquad\qquad f^{(2)}(0) = 2,$$

$$f^{(3)}(x) = \frac{6}{(1-x)^4}, \qquad\qquad f^{(3)}(0) = 6,$$

$$f^{(n)}(x) = \frac{n!}{(1-x)^{n+1}}, \qquad f^{(n)}(0) = n!\,.$$

It now follows that

$$\frac{1}{n!} f^{(n)}(0) = 1 \qquad (n = 0, 1, \cdots),$$

$$(1-x)^{-1} \sim \sum_0^\infty x^n = 1 + x + x^2 + \cdots\,.$$

This however is just the geometric series, and thus we see from Theorem 2c of Chapter 1 that the Maclaurin series for $1/(1-x)$ actually converges to to $1/(1-x)$ for $|x| < 1$. We can now write

$$(1-x)^{-1} = 1 + x + x^2 + x^3 + \cdots \qquad (|x| < 1)\,.$$

EXAMPLE 2. Let $f(x) = e^x$ and $c = 0$. Then we have

$$f(x) = e^x, \qquad f(0) = 1,$$
$$f'(x) = e^x, \qquad f'(0) = 1,$$
$$f^{(n)}(x) = e^x, \qquad f^{(n)}(0) = 1,$$

and thus

$$\frac{1}{n!} f^{(n)}(0) = \frac{1}{n!}\,.$$

The Maclaurin series generated by e^x is therefore

(6) $$e^x \sim \sum_0^\infty \frac{1}{n!} x^n = 1 + x + \tfrac{1}{2} x^2 + \tfrac{1}{6} x^3 + \cdots\,.$$

Using the methods of Sec. 9 of Chapter 1 it is easily verified that the series in (**6**) converges for all x ($\infty < x < \infty$). This still does not justify our writing

(**6'**) $$e^x = \sum_0^\infty \frac{1}{n!} x^n \qquad (-\infty < x < \infty)$$

since we have *not proved* that the sum the series converges to is e^x. In Sec. 3 we shall prove that (**6'**) is true; however, the proof requires altogether new ideas.

EXAMPLE 3. Let $f(x) = \cos x$ and $c = 0$. We have

$$\begin{aligned}
f(x) &= \cos x, & f(0) &= 1, \\
f'(x) &= -\sin x, & f'(0) &= 0, \\
f''(x) &= -\cos x, & f''(0) &= -1, \\
f'''(x) &= \sin x, & f'''(0) &= 0, \\
f^{(4)}(x) &= \cos x, & f^{(4)}(0) &= 1,
\end{aligned}$$

from which it follows that

(**7**) $$\cos x \sim \sum_0^\infty \frac{(-1)^n}{(2n)!} x^{2n} = 1 - \frac{1}{2}x^2 + \frac{1}{24}x^4 + \cdots.$$

EXAMPLE 4. If we take $f(x) = \sin x$ and $c = 0$, a computation similar to the preceding one gives

(**8**) $$\sin x \sim \sum_0^\infty \frac{(-1)^n x^{2n+1}}{(2n+1)!} = x - \frac{x^3}{3!} + \frac{x^5}{5!} - \frac{x^7}{7!} + \cdots.$$

EXAMPLE 5. Let $f(x) = \log x$ and $c = 1$. Here we find that

(**9**) $$\log x \sim \sum_1^\infty \frac{(-1)^{n-1}}{n} (x-1)^n.$$

The formulas (**6**) through (**9**) are so important and are of such frequent occurrence that they should be memorized.

In some cases the formulas for the successive derivatives become more and more complicated. However, even if one cannot find a general expression for the nth coefficient, one can compute any given number of terms in the Taylor series.

EXAMPLE 6. Compute the Taylor series of $\tan x$ about the center $x = \pi/4$ up through the term of index 3. We have

$$f(x) \quad = \tan x, \qquad\qquad\qquad f\left(\frac{\pi}{4}\right) = 1,$$

$$f'(x) \quad = \sec^2 x, \qquad\qquad\qquad f'\left(\frac{\pi}{4}\right) = 2,$$

$$f''(x) \quad = 2\sec^2 x \tan x, \qquad\qquad f''\left(\frac{\pi}{4}\right) = 4,$$

$$f'''(x) = 2\sec^4 x + 4\sec^2 x \tan^2 x, \quad f'''\left(\frac{\pi}{4}\right) = 16,$$

and thus

$$\tan x \sim 1 + 2\left(x - \frac{\pi}{4}\right) + 2\left(x - \frac{\pi}{4}\right)^2 + \frac{8}{3}\left(x - \frac{\pi}{4}\right)^3 + \cdots .$$

In high school it is shown that if n is a positive integer, then

$$(a + b)^n = \sum_{k=0}^{n} \binom{n}{k} a^{n-k} b^k ,$$

where

(10) $$\binom{n}{k} = \frac{n(n-1)\cdots(n-k+1)}{1 \cdot 2 \cdots k} .$$

[One can also write $\binom{n}{k} = \dfrac{n!}{(n-k)!k!}$. However we shall use the expression **(10)** which is valid whether n is an integer or not.] Note that $\binom{n}{0} = 1$ for all n. If we set $a = 1$, $b = x$, the above relation becomes

$$(1 + x)^n = \sum_{k=0}^{n} \binom{n}{k} x^k ,$$

(11) $$= \sum_{k=0}^{\infty} \binom{n}{k} x^k ,$$

since it follows from **(10)** that if n is an integer, then $\binom{n}{k} = 0$ whenever $k > n$. The formula **(11)** can thus be regarded as a power series expansion (with center 0) of $(1 + x)^n$. In the present section we shall prove

THEOREM 1b. Let n have any[1] real value; then

(12) $$(1 + x)^n \sim \sum_{k=0}^{\infty} \binom{n}{k} x^k .$$

[1] We shall exclude the value $n = 0$ because for this value the whole question is trivial.

Proof. We begin by noting that if $x \neq -1$, then

$$\left(\frac{d}{dx}\right)^k (1 + x)^n = n(n - 1) \cdots (n - k + 1) (1 + x)^{n-k}.$$

This is almost obvious since

$$\left(\frac{d}{dx}\right) (1 + x)^n = n(1 + x)^{n-1},$$

$$\left(\frac{d}{dx}\right)^2 (1 + x)^n = n(n - 1) (1 + x)^{n-2}, \text{ etc.}$$

Thus

$$\frac{1}{k!} \left(\frac{d}{dx}\right)^k (1 + x)^n \Big|_{x=0} = \binom{n}{k},$$

from which our theorem follows.

If n is a positive integer, the series (12) terminates with the term of index n in the sense that all the terms of higher index are 0. If n is not a positive integer, the series (12) does not terminate.

EXAMPLE 7. Expand $(1 + x)^{-2}$ in a Maclaurin series. We have

$$\binom{-2}{k} = \frac{(-2)(-3) \cdots (-2 - k + 1)}{1 \cdot 2 \cdot 3 \cdots \cdot k} = (-1)^k (k + 1).$$

Thus

$$(1 + x)^{-2} \sim \sum_0^\infty (-1)^k (k + 1) x^k.$$

PROBLEMS

Find the Taylor series about the prescribed center for each function listed below. In Problems 1–7 give the answer in the form "Σ."

1. $\log (1 + x)$ $(c = 0)$.
2. $(1 + x)^{-3}$ $(c = 0)$.
3. $(1 + x)^{1/2}$ $(c = 0)$.
4. $\log x$ $(c = 2)$.
5. $\sin x$ $(c = \pi)$.
6. e^x $(c = 1)$.
7. $(1 + x)^{-1}$ $(c = 1)$.

Find the first few terms of the Taylor series of each function listed below about the prescribed center, as in Example 6.

8. $\arctan x$ $(c = 0)$ (through the term of index 3).
9. $\log (1 + x^2)$ $(c = 0)$ (through the term of index 4).
10. $\sec x$ $(c = 0)$ (through the term of index 4),
11. $\sec x$ $(c = \pi/4)$ (through the term of index 2).
12. $\log (1 + e^{x-1})$ $(c = 1)$ (through the term of index 3).

13. $e^x \sin x$ $(c = 0)$ (through the term of index 3) .

14. e^{x^2} $(c = 0)$ (through the term of index 4) .

15. $\log \cos x$ $(c = \pi/4)$ (through the term of index 3) .

16. Show directly that if $P(x) = p_0 + p_1 x + p_2 x^2 + \cdots + p_n x^n$ is a polynomial of degree n, then for any real c, $P(x)$ can be written in the form

$$a_0 + a_1(x - c) + a_2(x - c)^2 + \cdots + a_n(x - c)^n .$$

Using the argument given at the beginning of this section, which in this context is rigorous, prove that

$$P(x) = \sum_0^\infty \frac{1}{k!} P^{(k)}(c) \, (x - c)^k .$$

This series, of course, terminates with the term of index n.

2. Elementary Transformations

In the present section we shall show how many Maclaurin series can be computed very simply if one knows certain standard series and certain rules of combination. The reader should keep firmly in mind that the problem is that of finding the Maclaurin series generated by a prescribed function. We are not here concerned with determining when such a series converges or to what it converges. All the operations described here apply with suitable modifications to Taylor series; we have confined our attention to Maclaurin series merely for the sake of definiteness.

Let us compute the Maclaurin series generated by $\sin x + \cos x$. We have, if $f(x) = \sin x + \cos x$,

$$
\begin{aligned}
f(x) &= + \sin x + \cos x , & f(0) &= 1 , \\
f^{(1)}(x) &= + \cos x - \sin x , & f^{(1)}(0) &= 1 , \\
f^{(2)}(x) &= - \sin x - \cos x , & f^{(2)}(0) &= - 1 , \\
f^{(3)}(x) &= - \cos x + \sin x , & f^{(3)}(0) &= - 1 , \\
f^{(4)}(x) &= + \sin x + \cos x , & f^{(4)}(0) &= 1 .
\end{aligned}
$$

Thus

(1) $$\sin x + \cos x \sim 1 + x - \frac{x^2}{2!} - \frac{x^3}{3!} + \frac{x^4}{4!} + \cdots .$$

By Examples 3 and 4 of Sec. 2 the Maclaurin series generated by $\cos x$ and by $\sin x$ are

$$\cos x \sim 1 + 0x - \frac{x^2}{2!} + 0x^3 + \frac{x^4}{4!} + \cdots ,$$

$$\sin x \sim 0 + x + 0x^2 - \frac{1}{3!} x^3 + 0x^4 + \cdots .$$

If these are added formally term by term as if they were polynomials, we obtain (1). This example suggests the following general result.

THEOREM 2a. If the Maclaurin series generated by $f(x)$ is

$$a_0 + a_1 x + a_2 x^2 + \cdots$$

and if the Maclaurin series generated by $g(x)$ is

$$b_0 + b_1 x + b_2 x^2 + \cdots,$$

then the Maclaurin series generated by $af(x) + bg(x)$ is

$$(aa_0 + bb_0) + (aa_1 + bb_1) x + (aa_2 + bb_2) x^2 + \cdots.$$

Equivalently the coefficient of x^n in the Maclaurin series for $af(x) + bg(x)$ is $aa_n + bb_n$.

Proof. By definition a_n, the coefficient of x^n in the Maclaurin series for $f(x)$, is

$$a_n = \frac{1}{n!} \left[\left(\frac{d}{dx} \right)^n f(x) \right]_{x=0},$$

and similarly

$$b_n = \frac{1}{n!} \left[\left(\frac{d}{dx} \right)^n g(x) \right]_{x=0}.$$

Again by definition the coefficient of x^n in the Maclaurin series for $af + bg$ is

$$\frac{1}{n!} \left[\left(\frac{d}{dx} \right)^n \{af(x) + bg(x)\} \right]_{x=0} = a \frac{1}{n!} \left[\left(\frac{d}{dx} \right)^n f(x) \right]_{x=0} + b \frac{1}{n!} \left[\left(\frac{d}{dx} \right)^n g(x) \right]_{x=0}$$

$$= aa_n + bb_n.$$

A fundamental formula of differential calculus asserts that

$$\frac{d}{dx} [f(x)g(x)[= f(x)g^{(1)}(x) + f^{(1)}(x)g(x).$$

Differentiating again and collecting terms, we find that

$$\left(\frac{d}{dx} \right)^2 f(x)g(x) = f(x)g^{(2)}(x) + 2f^{(1)}(x)g^{(1)}(x) + f^{(2)}(x)g(x).$$

Similarly

$$\left(\frac{d}{dx} \right)^3 f(x)g(x) = f(x)g^{(3)}(x) + 3f^{(1)}(x)g^{(2)}(x) + 3f^{(2)}(x)g^{(1)}(x) + f^{(3)}(x)g(x).$$

These results suggest that the formula

(2)
$$\left(\frac{d}{dx} \right)^n f(x)g(x) = \sum_{k=0}^{n} f^{(k)}(x) \, g^{(n-k)}(x) \binom{n}{k}$$

may hold true in general since as we have seen, it is valid for $n = 1, 2,$ and 3.

This is indeed the case, and it is easy to give a proof of (2) based upon induction. The identity (2) is known as Leibniz's formula.

THEOREM 2b. If the Maclaurin series for $f(x)$ is

$$a_0 + a_1 x + a_2 x^2 + a_3 x^3 + \cdots$$

and the Maclaurin series for $g(x)$ is

$$b_0 + b_1 + b_2 x^2 + b_3 x^3 + \cdots ,$$

then the Maclaurin series for $f(x)g(x)$ is

$$a_0 b_0 + (a_0 b_1 + a_1 b_0)\, x + (a_0 b_2 + a_1 b_1 + a_2 b_0)\, x^2 + \cdots .$$

Equivalently the coefficient of x^n in the Maclaurin series of $f(x)g(x)$ is $\sum_{k=0}^{n} a_k b_{n-k}$.

Another way of expressing this result is to say that if we multiply the Maclaurin series for $f(x)$ and the Maclaurin series for $g(x)$ as if they were polynomials, the result is the Maclaurin series for $f(x)g(x)$; that is,

$$b_0 + b_1 x + b_2 x^2 + \cdots$$
$$a_0 + a_1 x + a_2 x^2 + \cdots$$

$$\overline{}$$

$$a_0 b_0 + a_0 b_1 x + a_0 b_2 x^2 + \cdots$$
$$a_1 b_0 x + a_1 b_1 x^2 + \cdots$$
$$a_2 b_0 x^2 + \cdots$$

$$\overline{}$$

$$a_0 b_0 + (a_0 b_1 + a_1 b_0)\, x + (a_0 b_2 + a_1 b_1 + a_2 b_0)\, x^2 + \cdots .$$

Proof. The coefficient of x^n in the Maclaurin series for $f(x)g(x)$ is, using Leibnitz's rule,

$$\frac{1}{n!} \left[\left(\frac{d}{dx} \right)^n f(x)g(x) \right]_{x=0} = \frac{1}{n!} \sum_{k=0}^{n} \binom{n}{k} f^{(k)}(0)\, g^{(n-k)}(0)$$

$$= \sum_{k=0}^{n} \frac{1}{k!} f^{(k)}(0) \frac{1}{(n-k)!} g^{(n-k)}(0)$$

$$= \sum_{k=0}^{n} a_k b_{n-k} ,$$

as desired.

EXAMPLE 1. Compute the Maclaurin series of $e^x \sin(x + \alpha)$ through the term of index 3. Since $\sin(x + \alpha) = \sin x \cos \alpha + \cos x \sin \alpha$, we find, using Theorem 2a and Examples 3 and 4 of Sec. 1, that

$$\sin(x + \alpha) \sim \sin \alpha + (\cos \alpha)\, x - \tfrac{1}{2}(\sin \alpha)\, x^2 - \tfrac{1}{6}(\cos \alpha)\, x^3 + \cdots .$$

Multiplying this by the Maclaurin series for e^x,

$$e^x \sim 1 + x + \tfrac{1}{2}x^2 + \tfrac{1}{6}x^3 + \cdots ,$$

we obtain as our answer

$$\sin \alpha + (\sin \alpha + \cos \alpha)\,x + (\cos \alpha)\,x^2 + (\tfrac{1}{3}\cos \alpha - \tfrac{1}{3}\sin \alpha)\,x^3 + \cdots .$$

Using Theorem 2b, we find it possible to show that if $g(0) \neq 0$, the Maclaurin series for $f(x)/g(x)$ can be obtained by dividing the Maclaurin series of $g(x)$ formally into the Maclaur n series for $f(x)$.

EXAMPLE 2. Compute the Maclaurin series for $\tan x$ through the term of index 5. We have $\tan x = \sin x/\cos x$. Since

$$x + \tfrac{1}{3}x^3 + \tfrac{2}{15}x^5 + \cdots$$

$$1 - \tfrac{1}{2}x^2 + \tfrac{1}{24}x^4 + \cdots \overline{\smash{\big)}\ x - \tfrac{1}{6}x^3 + \tfrac{1}{120}x^5 + \cdots}$$

$$\underline{x - \tfrac{1}{2}x^3 + \tfrac{1}{24}x^5 + \cdots}$$

$$\tfrac{1}{3}x^3 \qquad\quad - \tfrac{1}{30}x^5 + \cdots$$

$$\underline{\tfrac{1}{3}x^3 \qquad\quad - \tfrac{1}{6}x^5 + \cdots}$$

$$\tfrac{2}{15}x^5 + \cdots$$

we see that

$$\tan x \sim x + \tfrac{1}{3}x^3 + \tfrac{2}{15}x^5 + \cdots .$$

THEOREM 2c. If the Maclaurin series for $f(x)$ is

$$a_0 + a_1 x + a_2 x^2 + \cdots ,$$

the Maclaurin series for $f(rx)$ is

$$a_1 + a(rx) + a_2(rx)^2 + \cdots .$$

Proof. We have

$$\left(\frac{d}{dx}\right) f(rx) = rf^{(1)}(rx) ,$$

$$\left(\frac{d}{dx}\right)^2 f(rx) = r^2 f^{(2)}(rx) ,$$

$$\left(\frac{d}{dx}\right)^n f(rx) = r^n f^{(n)}(rx) .$$

The coefficient of x^n in the Maclaurin series generated by $f(rx)$ is

$$\frac{1}{n!}\left(\frac{d}{dx}\right)^n [f(rx)]_{x=0} = \frac{1}{n!}\, r^n f^{(n)}(0) = r^n a_n ,$$

as desired.

EXAMPLE 3. Find the Maclaurin series generated by $(2x + 3)^{1/2}$ through the term of index 3. We have $(2x + 3)^{1/2} = [3(1 + 2x/3)]^{1/2} = 3^{1/2}(1 + 2x/3)^{1/2}$. By Theorem 1b

$$(1 + x)^{1/2} \sim 1 + \frac{\frac{1}{2}}{1!} x + \frac{\frac{1}{2}(-\frac{1}{2})}{2!} x^2 + \frac{(\frac{1}{2})(-\frac{1}{2})(-\frac{3}{2})}{3!} x^3 + \cdots.$$

Using Theorems 2a and 2c together, we find that

$$(2x + 3)^{1/2} \sim \sqrt{3} \left[1 + \frac{1}{2}\left(\frac{2x}{3}\right) - \frac{1}{8}\left(\frac{2x}{3}\right)^2 + \frac{1}{16}\left(\frac{2x}{3}\right)^3 + \cdots \right]$$

$$\sim \sqrt{3} + \frac{\sqrt{3}}{3} x - \frac{\sqrt{3}}{18} x^2 + \frac{\sqrt{3}}{54} x^3 + \cdots.$$

THEOREM 2d. If the Maclaurin series generated by $f(x)$ is

$$a_0 + a_1 x + a_2 x^2 + a_3 x^3 + \cdots,$$

the Maclaurin series generated by $f'(x)$ is

$$a_1 + 2a_2 x + 3a_3 x^2 + \cdots.$$

Proof. Left to the reader.

An equivalent formulation of Theorem 2d is that to obtain the Maclaurin series generated by $f'(x)$, differentiate the Maclaurin series generated by $f(x)$ formally term by term.

EXAMPLE 4. Since

$$(1 - x)^{-1} \sim 1 + x + x^2 + x^3 + x^4 + \cdots$$

and since $$(1 - x)^{-2} = \frac{d}{dx}(1 - x)^{-1},$$

we have $$(1 - x)^{-2} \sim 1 + 2x + 3x^2 + 4x^3 + \cdots.$$

It also follows from Theorem 2d that the Maclaurin series for $\int_0^x f(u) \, du$ can be obtained by integrating the Maclaurin series for $f(x)$ term by term from 0 to x.

EXAMPLE 5. Find the Maclaurin series for $\int_0^x \sin u \, du$. Since

$$\sin x \sim x - \frac{x^3}{3!} + \frac{x^5}{5!} + \cdots,$$

we have, by the remark above,

(3) $$\int_0^x \sin u \, du \sim \frac{x^2}{2!} - \frac{x^4}{4!} + \frac{x^6}{6!} + \cdots.$$

Since $\int_0^x \sin u \, du = \cos x - 1$, we can verify **(3)** directly.

PROBLEMS

Find the first few terms of the Maclaurin series generated by the functions listed below, using the methods of the present section.

1. $(1 - x)^{-1} - e^x$ (through the term of index 5).
2. $x \cos x - \sin x$ (through the term of index 5).
3. $\frac{1}{2}\sin 2x$ (through the term of index 5).
4. $\sin x \cos x$ (through the term of index 5).
5. $(\cos x)^2$ (through the term of index 6).
6. $(2x + 1)^{-2}$ (through the term of index 6).
7. $(3x + 5)^{3/2}$ (through the term of index 3).
8. $\sec x$ (through the term of index 3).
9. $\int_0^x e^{-u^2}\, du$ (through the term of index 5).
10. $\int_0^x \dfrac{2du}{1 + e^u}$ (through the term of index 4).

11. Prove that for any n, m

$$\sum_{j=0}^{k} \binom{n}{j} \binom{m}{k - j} = \binom{n + m}{k}.$$

HINT: Combine Theorems 1b and 2b.

3. The Remainder Formula

Let us consider the expression

(1) $$R_n(x) = \frac{1}{n!} \int_a^x f^{(n+1)}(t)\, (x - t)^n\, dt .$$

The reason for discussing $R_n(x)$ will become apparent in the sequel. Integrating by parts, we find that

$$R_n(x) = \frac{1}{n!} \left[f^{(n)}(t)(x - t)^n \right]_{t=a}^{t=x} + \frac{1}{(n - 1)!} \int_a^x f^{(n)}(t)\, (x - t)^{n-1}\, dt ,$$

(2) $$R_n(x) = - \left\{ \frac{f^{(n)}(a)}{n!}(x - a)^n \right\} + R_{n-1}(x) .$$

The formula (2) is true for any n; thus it remains true if we replace n by $n - 1$ in it to obtain

$$R_{n-1}(x) = - \left\{ \frac{f^{(n-1)}(a)}{(n - 1)!}(x - a)^{n-1} \right\} + R_{n-2}(x) .$$

Substituting this in (2), we find that

(3) $\quad R_n(x) = - \left\{ \dfrac{f^{(n)}(a)}{n!}(x-a)^n + \dfrac{f^{(n-1)}(a)}{(n-1)!}(x-a)^{n-1} \right\} + R_{n-2}(x).$

We next replace n by $n-2$ in (2) which gives

$$R_{n-2} = - \left\{ \dfrac{f^{(n-2)}(a)}{(n-2)!}(x-a)^{n-2} \right\} + R_{n-3}.$$

Substituting this in (3) gives

(4) $\quad R_n(x) = - \left\{ \dfrac{f^{(n)}(a)}{n!}(x-a)^n + \dfrac{f^{(n-1)}(a)}{(n-1)!}(x-a)^{n-1} + \dfrac{f^{(n-2)}(a)}{(n-2)!}(x-a)^{n-2} \right\}$

$\qquad + R_{n-3}(x).$

Proceeding in this way, we obtain after n steps

$$R_n(x) = - \left\{ \dfrac{f^{(n)}(a)}{n!}(x-a)^n + \cdots + \dfrac{f^{(1)}(a)}{1!}(x-a) \right\} + R_0(x).$$

The last step is slightly different. Instead of using (1) we examine $R_0(x)$ directly. We have

$$R_0(x) = \int_a^x f'(t)dt = f(x) - f(a).$$

Inserting this, we find that we have proved that

$$R_n(x) = - \left\{ \dfrac{f^{(n)}(a)}{n!}(x-a)^n + \cdots + \dfrac{f'(a)}{1!}(x-a) + f(a) \right\} + f(x).$$

Now the partial sum of index n of the Taylor series generated by $f(x)$ with center a is just

$$S_n(x) = f(a) + \dfrac{f'(a)}{1!}(x-a) + \cdots + \dfrac{f^{(n)}(a)}{n!}(x-a)^n.$$

Thus we see that we have established

THEOREM 3a. If $f(x)$ is continuous together with its derivatives of order $k(0 \le k \le n+1)$ in the interval $b_1 < x < b_2$ and if $b_1 < a$, $x < b_2$, then

$$f(x) = S_n(x) + R_n(x).$$

Thus $R_n(x)$ is the remainder of index n; that is, $R_n(x)$ is precisely the amount by which $S_n(x)$ falls short of $f(x)$, and to prove that $S_n(x) \to f(x)$

as $n \to \infty$ is clearly equivalent to proving that $R_n(x) \to 0$ as $n \to \infty$. Thus the formula of Theorem 3a affords us a method of proving that for certain functions $f(x)$ the Taylor series generated by $f(x)$ does converge to $f(x)$ for, of course, certain values of x.

In order to use Theorem 3a, we require certain auxiliary results.

LEMMA 3b. Let $a < b$; then for any function $F(u)$, $| \int_a^b F(u)\,du | \leq \int_a^b | F(u) |\,du$.

Let us examine a typical case (see Fig. 4).

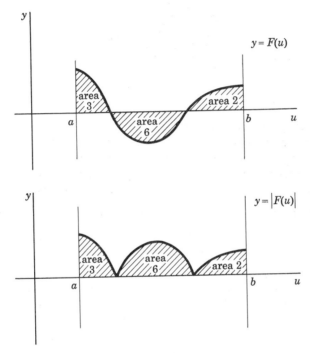

FIG. 4

In this case

$$\left| \int_a^b F(u)\,du \right| = |\,3 - 6 + 2\,| = 1\,,$$

whereas

$$\int_a^b | F(u) |\,du = 3 + 6 + 2 = 11\,.$$

Thus surely here

$$\left| \int_a^b F(u)\,du \right| \leq \int_a^b | F(u) |\,du\,.$$

Clearly the same idea applies in general, and we obtain our lemma.

LEMMA 3c. Let $a < b$; then if $G(u) \leq H(u)$ for $a \leq u \leq b$, we have (Fig. 5)

$$\int_a^b G(u) \, du \leq \int_a^b H(u) \, du \, .$$

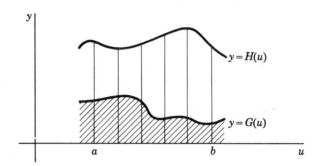

FIG. 5

This follows on comparing areas. Is the result still true if $a > b$? Why not?

We have given only intuitive proofs of Lemmas 3b and 3c. It is of course impossible to give a rigorous proof unless the Riemann (or Lebesgue) integral has been defined. Students familiar with the theory of Riemann integration should find it easy to write out correct proofs of these inequalities.

EXAMPLE 1. $f(x) = \sin x$ and $a = 0$. We have

$$R_n(x) = \frac{1}{n!} \int_0^x f^{(n+1)}(t) \, (x - t)^n \, dt \, .$$

Here $f^{(n+1)}(t)$ is some one of $\sin t$, $\cos t$, $-\sin t$, $-\cos t$. At all events $|f^{(n+1)}(t)| \leq 1$. Suppose first that $x \leq 0$. Then $x \leq t \leq 0$, and thus

$$|(x - t)^n| = (t - x)^n \, .$$

By Lemmas 3b and 3c we find that

(5) $$|R_n(x)| \leq \frac{1}{n!} \int_x^0 (t - x)^n \, dt = \frac{(-x)^{n+1}}{(n + 1)!} \, .$$

If $x \geq 0$, a similar argument gives

(5′) $$|R_n(x)| \leq \frac{x^{n+1}}{(n + 1)!} \, .$$

Here both inequalities may be subsumed under

(5″) $$|R_n(x)| \leq \frac{|x|^{n+1}}{(n + 1)!} \qquad (-\infty < x < \infty)$$

Let
$$u_n(x) = \frac{|x|^{n+1}}{(n+1)!} \, .$$

Then
$$\left| \frac{u_{n+1}(x)}{u_n(x)} \right| = \frac{|x|}{(n+2)} \, ,$$

and thus for any x,
$$\lim_{n \to \infty} \left| \frac{u_{n+1}(x)}{u_n(x)} \right| = 0 \, .$$

By Lemma 5d of Chapter 1 we see that for any x, $\lim_{n \to \infty} u_n(x) = 0$, and thus since $|R_n(x)| \le u_n(x)$, it follows that $\lim_{n \to \infty} R_n(x) = 0$ for any x. This implies that

$$\sin x = \sum_{n=0}^{\infty} (-1)^n \frac{x^{2n+1}}{(2n+1)!} \qquad (-\infty < x < \infty);$$

that is, the Maclaurin series *generated by* $\sin x$, *converges to* $\sin x$ for all real x

EXAMPLE 2. $f(x) = e^x$, $a = 0$. Here $f^{(n+1)}(t) = e^t$, and thus

$$R_n(x) = \frac{1}{n!} \int_0^x e^t (x-t)^n \, dt \, .$$

If $x \ge 0$, then $0 \le t \le x$ and $0 \le e^t \le e^x$. Thus

$$|e^t(x-t)^n| \le e^x(x-t)^n \, ,$$

and

$$|R_n(x)| \le \frac{1}{n!} \int_0^x e^x (x-t)^n \, dt = \frac{e^x \, x^{n+1}}{(n+1)!} \qquad (x \ge 0) \, .$$

If $x \ge 0$, then $x \le t \le 0$ and $0 \le e^t \le 1$. Thus

$$|e^t(x-t)^n| \le (t-x)^n \, ,$$

and the usual estimation process gives

$$|R_n(x)| \le \frac{(-x)^{n+1}}{(n+1)!} \qquad (x \le 0) \, .$$

Using Lemma 5d of Chapter 1, we see (considering the cases $x \ge 0$ and $x \le 0$ separately) that $\lim_{n \to \infty} R_n(x) = 0$ for every real x, and thus we have proved that

$$e^x = \sum_{n=0}^{\infty} \frac{x^n}{n!} \qquad (-\infty < x < \infty) \, .$$

Consider the problem of using the series above for e^x with $x = 2$ to compute e^2 correct to three decimal places with an error of at most one unit in the third

place. We know from earlier work that if we can find an index N for which $| R_N(2) | \leq 0.0005$ and if we then compute $S_N(2)$ to four or more places and round off to three, this will give us our answer. Now from the discussion of Example 2 we see that

$$| R_N(2) | \leq \frac{e^2 \, 2^{N+1}}{(N + 1)!}.$$

A short computation shows that if $N = 10$ (so that $N + 1 = 11$),

$$| R_{10}(2) | \leq \frac{e^2 \, 2^{11}}{11!} \leq 0.0005.$$

Since

$$\sum_0^{10} \frac{2^k}{k!} = 7.38881 \cdots,$$

it now follows that

$$\cdot \sum_0^{\infty} \frac{2^k}{k!} = 7.389 \pm 0.001.$$

Tables of exponentials give

$$e^2 = 7.3891 \cdots,$$

which affords a check of our computation.

PROBLEMS

1. Prove in detail that the Maclaurin series for $\cos x$ converges to $\cos x$ for $-\infty < x < \infty$.

2. Prove in detail that the Maclaurin series for $\sinh x$ converges to $\sinh x$ for $-\infty < x < \infty$.

3. Using the series of problem 2, compute $\sinh 1$ correct to two decimal places with an error of at most one unit in the second place.

4. Prove in detail that the Taylor series for $\sin x$ with center $\pi/4$ converges to $\sin x$ for $-\infty < x < \infty$.

5. Using the series of problem 4, compute $\sin (5\pi/12)$ correct to three decimal places with an error of at most one unit in the third place.

4. The Remainder Formula (Continued)

In this section we shall consider some important alternative forms for the remainder term R_n.

LEMMA 4a. If $\phi(t)$ and $\psi(t)$ are continuous for $a_1 \leq t \leq a_2$ and if $\psi(t)$ is of constant sign, there is a value $\xi(a_1 \leq \xi \leq a_2)$ for which

(1) $$\int_{a_1}^{a_2} \phi(t) \, \psi(t) \, dt = \phi(\xi) \int_{a_1}^{a_2} \psi(t) \, dt.$$

Proof. By assumption either $\psi(t) \geq 0$ for $a_1 \leq t \leq a_2$ or $\psi(t) \leq 0$ for $a_1 \leq t \leq a_2$. Let us assume for the sake of definiteness that $\psi(t) \geq 0$. Let M be the maximum, and m the minimum of $\phi(t)$ for $a_1 \leq t \leq a_2$. (See Theorem 2c of the Appendix.) By Lemma 3c we have

$$(2) \qquad m \int_{a_1}^{a_2} \psi(t)\, dt \leq \int_{a_1}^{a_2} \phi(t)\, \psi(t)\, dt \leq M \int_{a_1}^{a_2} \psi(t)\, dt \,.$$

Consider the function $\phi(x) \int_{a_1}^{a_2} \psi(t)\, dt$. Since it is a continuous function of x, it takes on all values between its minimum $m \int_{a_1}^{a_2} \psi(t)\, dt$ and its maximum $M \int_{a_1}^{a_2} \psi(t)\, dt$, see Theorem 2d of the Appendix. Thus in particular there is a value $\xi(a_1 \leq \xi \leq a_2)$ such that (1) holds.

It is to be noted that actually it is always possible to choose ξ so that $a_1 < \xi < a_2$. This may easily be demonstrated by carrying through the above argument with slightly greater attention to detail.

We can now derive two alternate forms for the remainder term R_n named after the mathematicians Lagrange and Cauchy, respectively.

THEOREM 4b. Let[1] $f(x) \in \mathbb{C}^{(n+1)}$ for $b_1 < x < b_2$, and let $b_1 < a$, $x < b_2$. If $R_n(x)$ is defined by the equation

$$f(x) = \sum_{k=0}^{n} \frac{f^{(k)}(a)}{k!} (x-a)^n + R_n(x)\,,$$

then for some value of ξ between a and x

$$(3) \qquad R_n(x) = \frac{f^{(n+1)}(\xi)}{(n+1)!} (x-a)^{n+1} \qquad \text{(Lagrange)},$$

and for some value of ζ between a and x

$$(4) \qquad R_n(x) = \frac{f^{(n+1)}(\zeta)}{n!} (x-\zeta)^n (x-a) \qquad \text{(Cauchy)}.$$

Proof. By Theorem 3a

$$R_n(x) = \frac{1}{n!} \int_a^x f^{(n+1)}(t) (x-t)^n\, dt \,.$$

To obtain (3), let $\phi(t) = f^{(n+1)}(t)$ and $\psi(t) = (x-t)^n$. By Lemma 4a there is a ξ between a and x such that

$$R_n(x) = f^{(n+1)}(\xi) \frac{1}{n!} \int_a^x (x-t)^n\, dt$$

$$= \frac{f^{(n+1)}(\xi)}{(n+1)!} (x-a)^{n+1} \,.$$

[1] $f(x) \in \mathbb{C}^{(n+1)}$ for $b_1 < x < b_2$ means that $f(x), f'(x), \ldots, f^{(n+1)}(x)$ are continuous for $b_1 < x < b_2$.

To obtain (4), let $\phi(t) = f^{(n+1)}(t) (x - t)^n$, and let $\psi(t) = 1$. By Lemma 4a there is a ζ between a and x such that

$$R_n(x) = f^{(n+1)}(\zeta) (x - \zeta)^n \frac{1}{n!} \int_a^x 1 \, dt$$

$$= \frac{f^{(n+1)}(\zeta)}{n!} (x - \zeta)^n (x - a).$$

In using the Lagrange (or Cauchy) form of the remainder we shall, of course, not know the value of ξ (or of ζ). Thus in order to obtain an explicit inequality for $R_n(x)$, it is necessary to replace $f^{(n+1)}(\xi)$ [or $f^{(n+1)}(\zeta) (x - \zeta)^n$] by the largest value it can have for ξ (or ζ) between a and x. Moreover since the Lagrange and Cauchy forms of the remainder are in effect simply methods for estimating the integral form of the remainder, any problem which can be solved using either can also be solved by careful use of the integral form. Nevertheless the Lagrange and Cauchy forms of the remainder are frequently very convenient.

EXAMPLE 1. Let $f(x) = \cosh x$, $a = 0$. Here $f^{(n+1)}(t)$ is $\sinh t$ or $\cosh t$. In any event $|f^{(n+1)}(t)| \leq \cosh t$. Using Lagrange's form of the remainder, we find that

$$R_n(x) = \frac{1}{(n + 1!)} f^{(n+1)} (\xi) x^{n+1}$$

where ξ is between 0 and x and thus

$$|R_n(x)| \leq \frac{x^{(n+1)}}{(n + 1)!} \cosh x \qquad (-\infty < x < \infty).$$

It is easily seen from this that $\lim_{n \to \infty} R_n(x) = 0$ for all x $(-\infty < x < \infty)$.

EXAMPLE 2. Let $f(x) = (1 + x)^{-5/2}$, $a = 0$. Here we have, see Theorem 1b,

$$f^{(n+1)}(t) = \left(-\frac{5}{2}\right) \left(-\frac{7}{2}\right) \cdots \left(-\frac{5}{2} - n\right) (1 + t)^{-(5/2)-n-1}.$$

It follows, using Cauchy's form of the remainder, that if $x > -1$,

$$R_n(x) = \frac{1}{n!} \left(-\frac{5}{2}\right) \left(-\frac{7}{2}\right) \cdots \left(-\frac{5}{2} - n\right) (1 + \zeta)^{-(5/2)-n-1} (x - \zeta)^n x$$

where ζ is between 0 and x. Suppose first that $0 \leq x < 1$; then

$$0 \leq (x - \zeta) \leq x, \qquad 0 \leq (1 + \zeta)^{-5/2-n-1} \leq 1,$$

and thus $| R_n(x) | \leq u_n(x)$ where

$$u_n(x) = \frac{1}{n!} \left(\frac{5}{2}\right) \left(\frac{7}{2}\right) \cdots \left(\frac{5}{2} + n\right) x^{n+1} .$$

Thus $u_{n+1}(x)/u_n(x) = \left(n + \frac{7}{2}\right) (n + 1)^{-1} x$ and $\lim\limits_{n \to \infty} u_{n+1}(x)/u_n(x) = x.$

Using Lemma 5d of Chapter 1, we see that $R_n(x) \to 0$ as $n \to \infty$ for $0 \leq x < 1.$ Next suppose that $-1 < x \leq 0$. Here

$$R_n(x) = \frac{1}{n!} \left(-\frac{5}{2}\right) \cdots \left(-\frac{5}{2} - n\right) \{(x - \zeta)(1 + \zeta)^{-1}\}^n (1 + \zeta)^{-7/2} x,$$

$$x \leq (x - \zeta)(1 + \zeta)^{-1} \leq 0, \qquad (1 + \zeta)^{-7/2} \leq (1 + x)^{-7/2} ,$$

and thus $| R_n(x) | \leq v_n(x)$ where

$$v_n(x) = \frac{1}{n!} \left(\frac{5}{2}\right) \left(\frac{7}{2}\right) \cdots \left(\frac{5}{2} + n\right) (1 + x)^{-7/2} | x |^{n+1} \qquad (-1 < x \leq 0).$$

Again it follows that $\lim\limits_{n \to \infty} R_n(x) = 0$ for $-1 \leq x < 0$. This example cannot be dealt with using Lagrange's form of the remainder. See **Problem 4**.

PROBLEMS

1. Use Lagrange's form of the remainder to obtain the estimates for $R_n(x)$ in the Maclaurin series for e^x which were obtained (differently) in Example 2 of Sec. 3.

2. Use Cauchy's form of the remainder to prove that the Taylor series for $\log x$ with center 1 converges to $\log x$ for $0 < x < 2$.

3. Use Cauchy's form of the remainder to prove that the Maclaurin series for $(4 + x)^{1/2}$ converges to $(4 + x)^{1/2}$ for $-4 < x < 4$.

4. Is it possible to prove, using Lagrange's form of the remainder, that the Maclaurin series for $(1 + x)^{-5/2}$ converges to $(1 + x)^{-5/2}$ if $0 \leq x < 1$? If $-1 < x \leq 0$? Explain.

5. Prove that for any $n \neq 0$ (n need not necessarily be an integer) the Maclaurin series for $(1 + x)^n$ converges to $(1 + x)^n$ for $-1 < x < 1$.

6. Prove that if p is a positive integer ($0 \leq p \leq n + 1$), then for some η between a and x

$$R_n = \frac{f^{(n+1)}(\eta) (x - \eta)^{n-p+1} (x - a)^p}{p \cdot n!} .$$

The case $p = n + 1$ is Lagrange's form of the remainder, and the case $p = 0$ is Cauchy's form of the remainder.

[3]

Fourier Series

1. Classes of Functions

The definition of a (real) function $f(\cdot)$ on an interval $a' \leq x \leq a''$ is that it is a rule by which to each number x in the interval $[a', a'']$ is associated a number $f(x)$. Usually such rules are given by formulas like

$$f(x) = x^2 - 2 \quad \text{or} \quad f(x) = (1 + e^x)^{1/2}.$$

However *any* rule defines a function whether it is given by a formula like the ones above or not. The class of all functions is, of course, too general to be of much interest, and usually attention is restricted to some subclass such as the set of all continuous functions or the set of all functions with continuous first derivatives. In our study of Fourier series we shall need to deal with the class of functions which are "piecewise continuous."

DEFINITION 1a. A function $f(x)$ defined on an interval $a' \leq x \leq a''$ is said to be piecewise continuous if there exist a finite number of points $a' = a_0 < a_1 < \cdots$ $a_n = a''$ and a corresponding set $f_1(x), f_2(x), \cdots, f_n(x)$ of functions, with $f_k(x)$ defined and continuous for $a_{k-1} \leq x \leq a_k$ such that

$$f(x) = f_k(x), \qquad a_{k-1} < x < a_k \qquad (k = 1, \cdots, n).$$

A function $f(x)$ defined on $(-\infty, \infty)$ is said to be piecewise continuous there if it is piecewise continuous on every finite subinterval $[a', a'']$.

A typical example of a piecewise continuous function is the following.

(1)
$$\phi(x) = \begin{cases} x^2 & (0 \leq x < 1) \\ -1 & (1 \leq x < 2) \\ 1 & (x = 2) \\ x - \dfrac{5}{2} & (2 < x < 3) \\ 0 & (x = 3) \end{cases}$$

We have Fig. 6.

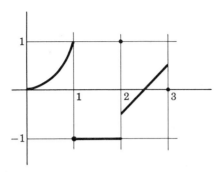

Fɪɢ. 6

Since piecewise continuous functions are given, so to speak, a piece at a time, the explicit evaluation of integrals involving these functions must be carried out by decomposing the range of integration into pieces such that within each piece the integrand is given by a simple formula.

EXAMPLE 1. Evaluate

$$I = \int_0^3 \phi(x) \, dx \, .$$

We have
$$I = \int_0^1 \phi(x) \, dx + \int_1^2 \phi(x) \, dx + \int_2^3 \phi(x) \, dx$$

$$= \int_0^1 x^2 \, dx + \int_1^2 (-1) \, dx + \int_2^3 \left(x - \frac{5}{2}\right) dx$$

$$= \left[\frac{x^3}{3}\right]_0^1 + \left[-x\right]_1^2 + \left[\frac{1}{2}\left(x - \frac{5}{2}\right)^2\right]_2^3 = -\frac{2}{3} \, .$$

Note that the values of $\phi(x)$ at the points where it is jointed (here $x = 0, 1,$ 2, 3) do not affect the value[1] of I.

DᴇꜰɪɴɪᴛɪᴏN 1b. Let $f(x)$ be a function defined for $-\infty < x < \infty$. Then $f(x)$ is said to be periodic with period $p \neq 0$ if $f(x) = f(x + p)$ for $-\infty < x < \infty$.

In intuitive language a function $f(x)$ has period p if by making a template of the graph of the function over any interval of length p, it is

[1] This is intuitively evident since the area contributed by a rectangle 0 units wide is 0. This fact is also easily demonstrated rigorously using the definition of the Riemann integral.

possible to graph f on the entire real axis by using the template again and again (Fig. 7.)

$p = 2$

$$-7/2 \qquad -3/2 \qquad o \ 1/2 \qquad 5/2 \qquad 9/2 \qquad 13/2$$

Fig. 7

DEFINITION 1c. A function $f(x)$ which is defined for $-\infty < x < \infty$ and is:
1. piecewise continuous,
2. periodic with period 2π,
will be said to belong to the class \mathfrak{F}; in symbols $f \in \mathfrak{F}$.

The class \mathfrak{F} is the set of functions for which we shall construct our theory. The functions

(2) $\qquad\qquad 1, \cos x, \sin x, \cos 2x, \sin 2x, \cos 3x, \sin 3x, \cdots$

all belong to \mathfrak{F}. They are, of course, all continuous and a fortiori piecewise continuous. They are also all periodic with period 2π. For example, if $f(x) = \sin 3x$, then

$$f(x + 2\pi) = \sin 3(x + 2\pi) = \sin(3x + 6\pi) = \sin 3x = f(x) .$$

EXAMPLE 2. Two further functions in \mathfrak{F} are

$$s(x) = \begin{cases} 1 & (0 < x < \pi) \\ 0 & (x = 0, \pi), \\ -1 & (\pi < x < 2\pi) \end{cases} \qquad s(x + 2\pi) = s(x)$$

and

$$t(x) = \pi - |x|, \qquad (-\pi \le x < \pi) \qquad t(x + 2\pi) = t(x) .$$

Fig. 8

The reader may think that functions such as $s(x)$ and $t(x)$ are "unnatural." However there are in many electronic devices (such as television sets) voltages which plotted against time look like the graphs in Fig. 8. Part of the significance of the theory of Fourier series lies in the fact that it constitutes an appropriate tool for dealing with such functions.

PROBLEMS

1. Let $f(x)$ and $g(x)$ be piecewise continuous functions defined for $a' \leq x \leq a''$. Are $f(x) + g(x)$ or $f(x) g(x)$ or both piecewise continuous? For the necessary facts concerning continuous functions see Sec. 2 of the Appendix.

2. Show that if $f(x)$ defined for $-\infty < x < \infty$ is periodic with period p, it is also periodic with period mp where m is any nonzero integer.

3. Show that if $f(x)$ defined for $-\infty < x < \infty$ is periodic with period p, so is $f(x + a)$ where a is any real number.

4. Show that if $f(x) \in \mathfrak{F}$, the integral of f over every interval of length 2π is the same.

5. Let $\phi(x)$ be defined as in Example 1.

Evaluate $$\int_0^3 x\, \phi(x)\, dx.$$

Let $s(x)$ and $t(x)$ be defined as in Example 2.

6. Evaluate $$\int_{-\pi}^{\pi} s^2(x)\, dx.$$

7. Evaluate $$\int_{\pi/2}^{3\pi/2} t^2(x)\, dx.$$

8. Evaluate $$\int_0^{2\pi} s(x)\, t(x)\, dx.$$

9. Evaluate $$\int_0^{2\pi} s(x)\, s\left(x + \frac{\pi}{4}\right) dx.$$

10. Evaluate $$\int_0^{2\pi} t(x)\, t\left(x - \frac{\pi}{4}\right) dx.$$

2. Fourier Series

The functions

(1) $$1,\ \sin x,\ \cos x,\ \sin 2x,\ \cos 2x,\ \cdots$$

all belong to \mathfrak{F}. It is evident that by taking finite linear combinations of these functions, we can construct additional functions in \mathfrak{F}. An evident generalization of such finite linear combinations are infinite series of the form

(2) $$\frac{a_0}{2} + (a_1 \cos x + b_1 \sin x) + (a_2 \cos 2x + b_2 \sin 2x) + \cdots .$$

The question now arises, can any reasonably well-behaved periodic function $f(x)$ with period 2π be represented as a series of the form (**2**)? Of course for this to be possible it is necessary that the constants $a_0, a_1, b_1, a_2, b_2, \cdots$ be chosen correctly, their choice depending on the function $f(x)$ to be expanded. Our first problem is to try to guess what this correct choice is. We begin by recalling the following formulas. Here m, n are nonnegative integers.

$$(\mathbf{3_1}) \qquad \int_{-\pi}^{\pi} \cos nx \cos mx \, dx = \begin{cases} 0 & (n \neq m) \\ \pi & (n = m \neq 0) \\ 2\pi & (n = m = 0), \end{cases}$$

$$(\mathbf{3_2}) \qquad \int_{-\pi}^{\pi} \cos nx \sin mx \, dx = 0,$$

$$(\mathbf{3_3}) \qquad \int_{-\pi}^{\pi} \sin nx \sin mx \, dx = \begin{cases} 0 & (n \neq m) \\ \pi & (n = m \geq 1). \end{cases}$$

We shall prove (**3₁**). Recalling the formulas

$$\cos (A + B) = \cos A \cos B - \sin A \sin B,$$

$$\cos (A - B) = \cos A \cos B + \sin A \sin B$$

and adding, we obtain

$$\cos A \cos B = \tfrac{1}{2} \cos (A + B) + \tfrac{1}{2} \cos (A - B).$$

Thus

$$\int_{-\pi}^{\pi} \cos nx \cos mx \, dx = \tfrac{1}{2} \int_{-\pi}^{\pi} \cos (n + m)x \, dx + \tfrac{1}{2} \int_{-\pi}^{\pi} \cos(n - m)x \, dx.$$

Suppose first that $m \neq n$. Then

$$\int_{-\pi}^{\pi} \cos nx \cos mx \, dx = \tfrac{1}{2} \left[\frac{\sin(n + m)x}{n + m} \right]_{-\pi}^{\pi} + \tfrac{1}{2} \left[\frac{\sin(n - m)x}{n - m} \right]_{-\pi}^{\pi} = 0.$$

Suppose next that $n = m \neq 0$. Then

$$\int_{-\pi}^{\pi} \cos nx \cos mx \, dx = \tfrac{1}{2} \left[\frac{\sin 2nx}{2n} \right]_{-\pi}^{\pi} + \tfrac{1}{2} \left[x \right]_{-\pi}^{\pi} = \pi.$$

Finally if $n = m = 0$,

$$\int_{-\pi}^{\pi} \cos nx \cos mx \, dx = \int_{-\pi}^{\pi} 1 \, dx = 2\pi.$$

The remaining formulas are left to the reader as exercises.

Let us now *assume* that

(4) $$f(x) = \frac{a_0}{2} + \sum_{k=1}^{\infty} (a_k \cos kx + b_k \sin kx).$$

Multiply both sides of (4) by cos nx and integrate from over the interval from $-\pi$ to π. Treating the infinite series on the right as if it were a finite series (sum) so that term by term integration is permissible, we find that

$$\int_{-\pi}^{\pi} f(x) \cos nx\, dx = \frac{a_0}{2} \int_{-\pi}^{\pi} \cos nx\, dx + a_1 \int_{-\pi}^{\pi} \cos x \cos nx\, dx$$

$$+ b_1 \int_{-\pi}^{\pi} \sin x \cos nx\, dx + a_2 \int_{-\pi}^{\pi} \cos 2x \cos nx\, dx$$

$$+ b_2 \int_{-\pi}^{\pi} \sin 2x \cos nx\, dx + \cdots.$$

Now because of (3_1) and (3_2) all the integrals on the right are zero except one, and we obtain

(5_1) $$\int_{-\pi}^{\pi} f(x) \cos nx\, dx = \pi a_n \qquad (n = 0, 1, \cdots).$$

(That this formula also holds for $n = 0$ is because of the peculiar $\frac{1}{2}$ factor written with a_0.) Similarly multiplying (4) by sin nx, etc., we find that

(5_2) $$\int_{-\pi}^{\pi} f(x) \sin nx\, dx = b_n \qquad (n = 1, 2, \cdots).$$

DEFINITION 2a. Let $f(x) \in \mathfrak{F}$. If the constants $a_0, a_1, b_1, a_2, b_2, \cdots$ are computed from the formulas (5_1) and (5_2), the series (2) is called the "Fourier series" of the function $f(x)$.

Notice that the situation here is exactly like that in Sec. 1 of Chapter 2; that is, we have a rule that enables us to associate with each function of a certain class a series. Although we may hope that the series will converge to the function in question, the argument we have given is suggestive rather than rigorous. Later we shall show that under very general conditions the Fourier series of a function $f(x) \in \mathfrak{F}$ does indeed converge to $f(x)$. However in this section and in the next we shall deal only with the problem of computing the Fourier series of a given function. To emphasize the fact that no question of convergence is involved, we write

$$f(x) \sim \tfrac{1}{2}a_0 + \sum_{n=1}^{\infty} (a_n \cos nx + b_n \sin nx)$$

if the a_n's and b_n's are given by (5_1) and (5_2).

EXAMPLE 1. Compute the Fourier series of $s(x)$ as defined in Sec. 1. Before making the actual computation, it will be convenient to make some general observations which apply to many problems of this kind. A function $\phi(x)$ defined on an interval $(-a \leq x \leq a)$ symmetric with respect to the origin is said to be *even* if $\phi(x) = \phi(-x)$ $0 \leq x \leq a$ and to be *odd* if $\phi(x) = -\phi(-x)$ $0 \leq x \leq a$ (Fig. 9.)

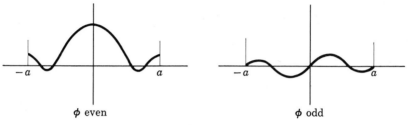

ϕ even ϕ odd

FIG. 9

The following facts concerning even and odd functions are immediately verifiable.

1. Any linear combination of even (odd) functions is again even (odd).

2. The product of two even or two odd functions is even, whereas the product of an even function and an odd function is odd.

3.
$$\int_{-a}^{a} \phi(x)\, dx = 2 \int_{0}^{a} \phi(x)\, dx \qquad \text{if } \phi \text{ is even,}$$

$$\int_{-a}^{a} \phi(x)\, dx = 0 \qquad \text{if } \phi \text{ is odd.}$$

Finally we note that the functions $\cos nx$ ($n = 0, 1, 2, \cdots$) are all even whereas the functions $\sin nx$ ($n = 1, 2, \cdots$) are all odd.

We now return to our example. By Fact 2 above the functions $\cos nx\, s(x)$ ($n = 0, 1, \cdots$) are all odd and therefore by Fact 3 the integrals ($\mathbf{5}_1$) all vanish. On the other hand the functions $\sin nx\, s(x)$ ($n = 1, 2, \cdots$) are even, and therefore by Fact 3

$$\frac{1}{\pi} \int_{-\pi}^{\pi} \sin nx\, s(x) = \frac{2}{\pi} \int_{0}^{\pi} \sin nx\, s(x)\, dx$$

$$= \frac{2}{\pi} \int_{0}^{\pi} \sin nx\, dx$$

$$= \frac{2}{\pi} \left[\frac{-\cos nx}{n} \right]_{0}^{\pi} = \frac{2}{\pi n} \left[1 - \cos n\pi \right]$$

$$= \begin{cases} \dfrac{4}{\pi n} & \text{if } n = 1, 3, 5, \cdots \\ 0 & \text{if } n = 2, .4, 6, \cdots. \end{cases}$$

Thus

$$s(x) \sim \frac{4}{\pi} \sin x + \frac{4}{3\pi} \sin 3x + \frac{4}{5\pi} \sin 5x + \cdots$$

$$\sim \frac{4}{\pi} \sum_{k=0}^{\infty} (2k + 1)^{-1} \sin (2k + 1)x.$$

EXAMPLE 2. Compute the Fourier series of $t(x)$ as defined in Sec. 1. The function $t(x)$ is even and thus $b_n = 0$ $(n = 1, 2, \cdots)$, and

$$a_n = \frac{2}{\pi} \int_0^{\pi} (\pi - x) \cos nx \, dx$$

$$= \left[\frac{2}{\pi} (\pi - x) \frac{\sin nx}{n} \right]_0^{\pi} + \frac{2}{\pi n} \int_0^{\pi} \sin nx \, dx = \frac{2}{\pi n} \left[- \frac{\cos nx}{n} \right]_0^{\pi}$$

$$= \begin{cases} \dfrac{4}{\pi n^2} & (n \text{ is odd}) \\ 0 & (n \text{ is even, } n \neq 0). \end{cases}$$

A separate computation yields

$$a_0 = \pi.$$

Thus

$$t(x) \sim \frac{\pi}{2} + \frac{4}{\pi} \sum_{n=0}^{\infty} (2n + 1)^{-2} \cos (2n + 1)x.$$

If $f \in \mathfrak{F}$, then since it is periodic with period 2π it is completely determined for $-\infty < x < \infty$ when its values in the interval $-\pi \leq x < \pi$ are given.

PROBLEMS

Find the Fourier series of the following functions, all belonging to \mathfrak{F}.

1. $f(x) = x$ $(-\pi \leq x < \pi)$.

2. $f(x) = \cos cx$ $(-\pi \leq x < \pi, \;\; 0 < c < 1)$.

3. $f(x) = |\sin x|$ $(-\pi \leq x < \pi)$.

4. $f(x) = \sin^2 x$ $(-\pi \leq x < \pi)$.

5. $f(x) = x^2$ $(-\pi \leq x < \pi)$.

6. $f(x) = \begin{cases} x \\ 0 \end{cases}$ $\begin{matrix} (-\pi \leq x < 0) \\ (0 \leq x < \pi). \end{matrix}$

7. $f(x) = x \sin x,$ $(-\pi \leq x < \pi)$.

8. $f(x) = \begin{cases} 0 \\ \cos x \\ 0 \end{cases}$ $\begin{matrix} \left(-\pi \leq x < -\dfrac{\pi}{2}\right) \\ \left(-\dfrac{\pi}{2} < x < \dfrac{\pi}{2}\right) \\ \left(\dfrac{\pi}{2} < x < \pi\right). \end{matrix}$

9. Prove that if $f, g \in \mathfrak{F}$ and

$$f(x) \sim \frac{a_0}{2} + \sum_{n=1}^{\infty} a_n \cos nx + b_n \sin nx \, ,$$

$$g(x) \sim \frac{c_0}{2} + \sum_{n=1}^{\infty} c_n \cos nx + d_n \sin nx \, ,$$

then $\qquad rf(x) + sg(x) \sim \dfrac{ra_0 + sc_0}{2} + \sum_{n=1}^{\infty} (ra_n + sc_n) \cos nx$

$$+ (rb_n + sd_n) \sin nx.$$

10. Prove that if $f \in \mathfrak{F}$ and

$$f(x) \sim \frac{a_0}{2} + \sum_{n=1}^{\infty} a_n \cos nx + b_n \sin nx$$

and if f' is piecewise continuous, then $f' \in \mathfrak{F}$ and

$$f'(x) \sim \sum_{n=1}^{\infty} n \, b_n \cos nx - na_n \sin nx.$$

11. Prove that if $f(x)$ is a trigonometric polynomial, that is, a finite linear combination of the functions (**1**), and if

$$f(x) \sim \tfrac{1}{2}a_0 + \sum_{n=1}^{\infty} a_n \cos nx + b_n \sin nx,$$

then for $-\infty < x < \infty$

$$f(x) = \tfrac{1}{2}a_0 + \sum_{n=1}^{\infty} a_n \cos nx + b_n \sin nx.$$

3. Bessel's Inequality

THEOREM 3a. (Bessel's inequality.) If

1. $f(x) \in \mathfrak{F}$,

2. $f(x) \sim \tfrac{1}{2}a_0 + \sum_{n=1}^{\infty} a_n \cos nx + b_n \sin nx,$

then

(1)
$$\tfrac{1}{2}a_0^2 + \sum_{n=1}^{\infty} (a_n^2 + b_n^2) \leq \frac{1}{\pi} \int_{-\pi}^{\pi} f(x)^2 \, dx.$$

Proof. Choose a nonnegative integer N, and consider

(2)
$$S_N(x) = \tfrac{1}{2}a_0 + \sum_{n=1}^{N} a_n \cos nx + b_n \sin nx,$$

$$R_N(x) = f(x) - S_N(x).$$

Using the formulas **(3)** of Sec. 2, we see that

$$\frac{1}{\pi} \int_{-\pi}^{\pi} [f(x) - S_N(x)] \cos nx \, dx = a_n - a_n = 0 \qquad (n = 0, 1, \cdots, N),$$

$$\frac{1}{\pi} \int_{-\pi}^{\pi} [f(x) - S_N(x)] \sin nx \, dx = b_n - b_n = 0 \qquad (n = 1, \cdots, N).$$

From these relations it follows that

(3)
$$\frac{1}{\pi} \int_{-\pi}^{\pi} [f(x) - S_N(x)] \, \psi_N(x) \, dx = 0$$

if ψ_N is any trigonometric polynomial of order N, that is, if ψ_N is of the form

$$\psi_N(x) = \tfrac{1}{2}c_0 + \sum_{n=1}^{N} c_n \cos nx + d_n \sin nx$$

where the constants $c_0, c_1, d_1, \cdots, c_n, d_n$ are any real numbers. In particular we may set $\psi_N(x) = S_N(x)$ to obtain

(4)
$$\frac{1}{\pi} \int_{-\pi}^{\pi} [f(x) - S_N(x)] \, S_N(x) \, dx = 0.$$

On the other hand we may verify that

(5)
$$\frac{1}{\pi} \int_{-\pi}^{\pi} S_N(x)^2 \, dx = \tfrac{1}{2}a_0^2 + \sum_{n=1}^{N} (a_n^2 + b_n^2);$$

to see this, square $S_N(x)$, given by **(2)**, and integrate from $-\pi$ to π. Because of the formulas **(3)** of Sec. 2 all the cross-product terms drop out and we obtain **(5)**. We can now prove **(1)**. We have

$$\frac{1}{\pi} \int_{-\pi}^{\pi} f(x)^2 \, dx = \frac{1}{\pi} \int_{-\pi}^{\pi} [(f(x) - S_N(x)) + S_N(x)]^2 \, dx$$

$$= \frac{1}{\pi} \int_{-\pi}^{\pi} [f(x) - S_N(x)]^2 \, dx + \frac{2}{\pi} \int_{-\pi}^{\pi} [f(x) - S_N(x)] \, S_N(x) \, dx$$

$$+ \frac{1}{\pi} \int_{-\pi}^{\pi} S_N(x)^2 \, dx$$

$$= \frac{1}{\pi} \int_{-\pi}^{\pi} [f(x) - S_N(x)]^2 \, dx + \tfrac{1}{2}a_0^2 + \sum_{n=1}^{N} (a_n^2 + b_n^2)$$

$$\geq \tfrac{1}{2}a_0^2 + \sum_{n=1}^{N} (a_n^2 + b_n^2).$$

Applying Axiom 1a of the Appendix, we obtain (1).

COROLLARY 3b. (Riemann-Lebesgue.) If $f(x)$ is a piecewise continuous function for $-\pi \leq x < \pi$, then

(6)
$$\lim_{n \to \infty} \frac{1}{\pi} \int_{-\pi}^{\pi} f(x) \cos nx \, dx = 0,$$

$$\lim_{n \to \infty} \frac{1}{\pi} \int_{-\pi}^{\pi} f(x) \sin nx \, dx = 0.$$

This follows from (1) and Theorem 3d of Chapter 1.

The following result is closely related to Theorem 3a.

THEOREM 3c. Let $f \in \mathfrak{F}$, and let S_N be defined by (2). Then if ϕ_N is any trigonometric polynomial of degree N,

(7)
$$\frac{1}{\pi} \int_{-\pi}^{\pi} [f(x) - \phi_N(x)]^2 \, dx \geq \frac{1}{\pi} \int_{-\pi}^{\pi} [f(x) - S_N(x)]^2 \, dx$$

with equality only if $\phi_N(x) \equiv S_N(x)$.

Proof. This result asserts that in a certain average sense $S_N(x)$ is of all trigonometric polynomials of order N the one which best approximates $f(x)$. We have

(8) $\dfrac{1}{\pi} \displaystyle\int_{-\pi}^{\pi} [f(x) - \phi_N(x)]^2 \, dx = \dfrac{1}{\pi} \displaystyle\int_{-\pi}^{\pi} [\{f(x) - S_N(x)\} + \{S_N(x) - \phi_N(x)\}]^2 \, dx$

$$= \frac{1}{\pi} \int_{-\pi}^{\pi} [f(x) - S_N(x)]^2 \, dx +$$

$$\frac{1}{\pi} \int_{-\pi}^{\pi} [S_N(x) - \phi_N(x)]^2 \, dx$$

since the cross-product term vanishes, see (3). The inequality (7) is an easy consequence of (8).

Returning to Theorem 3a, we remark that in point of fact if $f \in \mathfrak{F}$, then

(9)
$$\tfrac{1}{2}a_0^2 + \sum_{n=1}^{\infty} (a_n^2 + b_n^2) = \frac{1}{\pi} \int_{-\pi}^{\pi} f(x)^2 \, dx.$$

This result, referred to as "Parseval's equality," will be proved in Chapter 7. It is a much deeper result than Bessel's inequality. In spite of this let us use **(9)** now without proof. By means of it we can find explicitly the sums of many interesting series.

EXAMPLE 1. Evaluate $\sum_{k=0}^{\infty} (2k + 1)^{-2}$. We apply Parseval's equality **(9)** to the function $s(x)$. Referring to Example 1 of Sec. 2, we see that

$$\sum_{k=0}^{\infty} \left[\frac{4}{\pi(2k + 1)} \right]^2 = \frac{1}{\pi} \int_{-\pi}^{\pi} s(x)^2 \, dx = 2$$

so that

$$\sum_{k=0}^{\infty} (2k + 1)^{-2} = \frac{\pi^2}{8}.$$

PROBLEMS

1. Evaluate the series $\sum_{n=0}^{\infty} (2n + 1)^{-4}$ by applying Parseval's equality to the function $t(x)$.

2. Apply Parseval's equality to the function $f(x) = x$ for $-\pi \leq x < \pi$.

3. Apply Parseval's equality to the function $f(x) = \cos cx$ for $-\pi \leq x < \pi$ where $0 < c < 1$.

4. Apply Parseval's equality to the function $f(x) = |\sin x|$ for $-\pi \leq x < \pi$.

4. Dirichlet's Formula

The present section is devoted to obtaining a fundamental formula for $R_N(x)$, the remainder of index N of a given Fourier series. Let us define

(1)
$$D_N(t) = \tfrac{1}{2} + \cos t + \cos 2t + \cdots + \cos Nt.$$

$D_N(t)$ is called the Dirichlet kernel of index N. It is evident that

(2)
$$D_N(t + 2\pi) = D_N(t)$$

and that

(3)
$$\frac{1}{\pi} \int_{-\pi}^{\pi} D_N(t) \, dt = 1.$$

THEOREM 4a. Let $f \in \mathfrak{F}$, let $R_N(x)$ be defined by (2) in Sec. 3, and $D_N(t)$ by (1); then

$$R_N(x) = \frac{1}{\pi} \int_{-\pi}^{\pi} [f(x) - f(x - t)] D_N(t) \, dt.$$

Proof. We have

$$S_N(x) = \tfrac{1}{2}a_0 + a_1 \cos x + b_1 \sin x + \cdots + a_N \cos Nx + b_N \sin Nx.$$

Inserting for each coefficient its formula, we obtain

$$S_N(x) = \tfrac{1}{2}\frac{1}{\pi} \int_{-\pi}^{\pi} f(t) \, dt + \cos x \frac{1}{\pi} \int_{-\pi}^{\pi} f(t) \cos t \, dt + \sin x \frac{1}{\pi} \int_{-\pi}^{\pi} f(t) \sin t \, dt$$

$$+ \cdots + \cos Nx \frac{1}{\pi} \int_{-\pi}^{\pi} f(t) \cos Nt \, dt + \sin Nx \frac{1}{\pi} \int_{-\pi}^{\pi} f(t) \sin Nt \, dt.$$

Combining integrals, we find that

$$S_N(x) = \frac{1}{\pi} \int_{-\pi}^{\pi} f(t) [\tfrac{1}{2} + \cos x \cos t + \sin x \sin t + \cdots$$

$$+ \cos Nx \cos Nt + \sin Nx \sin Nt] \, dt$$

$$= \frac{1}{\pi} \int_{-\pi}^{\pi} f(t) [\tfrac{1}{2} + \cos(x - t) + \cdots + \cos N(x - t)] \, dt.$$

Here we have used

$$\cos kx \cos kt + \sin kx \sin kt = \cos k(x - t).$$

Referring to (1), we see that

$$S_N(x) = \frac{1}{\pi} \int_{-\pi}^{\pi} f(t) D_N(x - t) \, dt.$$

Setting $x - t = u$ yields

$$S_N(x) = \frac{1}{\pi} \int_{x-\pi}^{x+\pi} f(x - u) D_N(u) \, du$$

(4)
$$= \int_{-\pi}^{\pi} f(x - u) D_N(u) \, du.$$

In the last step we have used Problem 4 of Sec. 1. By (3)

$$f(x) = f(x) \frac{1}{\pi} \int_{-\pi}^{\pi} D_N(u) \, du$$

(5)
$$= \frac{1}{\pi} \int_{-\pi}^{\pi} f(x) D_N(u) \, du.$$

Recalling that $R_N(x) = f(x) - S_N(x)$ and subtracting (4) from (5), we obtain our desired result.

We next obtain a closed expression for $D_N(x)$.

LEMMA 4b. If N is a nonnegative integer, then

(6) $$D_N(x) = \frac{\sin(N + \frac{1}{2})x}{2 \sin (x/2)}$$

if $x \neq 0, \pm 2\pi, \pm 4\pi, \cdots$

Proof. We shall prove (6) by induction. If $N = 0$, then (6) is clearly true since both sides reduce to $\frac{1}{2}$. Let us assume that (6) is valid for $N - 1$; we shall show that it is then valid for N. By assumption

(7) $$\frac{1}{2} + \cos x + \cdots + \cos(N - 1)x = \frac{\sin(N - \frac{1}{2})x}{2 \sin (x/2)}.$$

Adding $\cos Nx$ to both sides, we obtain

$$\frac{1}{2} + \cos x \cdots + \cdot + \cos (n - 1) x + \cos Nx = \frac{\sin(N - \frac{1}{2}) x}{2 \sin(x/2)} + \cos Nx$$

$$= \frac{\sin(N - \frac{1}{2}) x + 2 \sin (x/2) \cos Nx}{2 \sin(x/2)}.$$

Now by the trigonometric addition formulas

$$\sin(N - \tfrac{1}{2}) x = \sin Nx \cos \frac{x}{2} - \cos Nx \sin \frac{x}{2},$$

$$\sin (N + \tfrac{1}{2}) x = \sin Nx \cos \frac{x}{2} + \cos Nx \sin \frac{x}{2}$$

$$= \sin(N - \tfrac{1}{2}) x + 2 \sin \frac{x}{2} \cos Nx.$$

Using this we see that if (7) holds, then (6) is valid. Our induction is now complete.

PROBLEMS

1. Prove that

$$\sin x + \sin 2x + \cdots + \sin(N - 1) x + \tfrac{1}{2}\sin Nx = \frac{\sin x [1 - \cos Nx]}{2(1 - \cos x)}.$$

2. Prove that

$$\sin \frac{x}{2} + \sin \frac{3x}{2} + \cdots + \sin \frac{2N + 1}{2} x = \frac{\sin^2[x(N + 1)/2]}{\sin(x/2)}.$$

5. A Convergence Theorem

In this section we shall prove that if $f \in \mathfrak{F}$, the Fourier series of f will converge to f at any point x_0 at which f is differentiable. Although weaker conditions than differentiability are sufficient to ensure convergence, some such condition is necessary.

LEMMA 5a. If

1. $f(x) \in \mathfrak{F}$,

2. $f'(x_0)$ exists,

then the function $\psi_{x_0}(u)$ which is defined as $[-f(x_0 - u) + f(x_0)]/2 \sin (u/2)$ if $u \neq 0$ and as $f'(x_0)$ if $u = 0$ is a piecewise continuous function of u for $-\pi \leq u \leq \pi$.

Proof. This is almost obvious. The only point that can cause difficulty is $u = 0$. But $\psi_{x_0}(u)$ is continuous at $u = 0$. Use L'Hôpital's rule!

THEOREM 5b. If

1. $f(x) \in \mathfrak{F}$,

2. $S_N(x)$ is defined as in (2) of Sec. 3,

3. $f'(x_0)$ exists,

then $\lim\limits_{N \to \infty} S_N(x_0) = f(x_0)$.

Proof. By Theorem 4a

$$R_N(x_0) = \frac{1}{\pi} \int_{-\pi}^{\pi} [-f(x_0 - u) + f(x_0)] D_N(u) \, du \, .$$

By Lemmas 5a and 4b we see that for $-\pi \leq u \leq \pi$

$$[-f(x_0 - u) + f(x_0)] D_N(u) = \psi_{x_0}(u) \sin (N + \tfrac{1}{2}) u.$$

This is evident except possibly for $u = 0$, but here both sides of the above equation vanish. Thus using

$$\sin(N + \tfrac{1}{2}) u = \sin Nu \cos \frac{u}{2} + \cos Nu \sin \frac{u}{2} \, ,$$

we find that

$$R_N(x_0) = \frac{1}{\pi} \int_{-\pi}^{\pi} \psi_{x_0}(u) \cos \frac{u}{2} \sin Nu \, du$$

$$+ \frac{1}{\pi} \int_{-\pi}^{\pi} \psi_{x_0}(u) \sin \frac{u}{2} \cos Nu \, du \, .$$

Here $\psi_{x_0}(u) \cos (u/2)$ and $\psi_{x_0}(u) \sin (u/2)$ are piecewise continuous functions, and thus Corollary 3b implies that

$$\lim_{N \to \infty} R_N(x_0) = 0 ,$$

as desired.

EXAMPLE 1. Sum the series

$$\sum_{k=0}^{\infty} \frac{(-1)^{k-1}}{2k+1} = 1 - \frac{1}{3} + \frac{1}{5} - \frac{1}{7} + \cdots .$$

By Example 1 of Sec. 2 we have

$$s(x) \sim \frac{4}{\pi} \sum_{k=0}^{\infty} (2k+1)^{-1} \sin(2k+1) \, x .$$

the function $s(x) \in \mathfrak{F}$ and is differentiable at $x = \pi/2$; therefore by Theorem 5b

$$s\left(\frac{\pi}{2}\right) = \frac{4}{\pi} \sum_{k=0}^{\infty} (2k+1)^{-1} \sin\left[(2k+1) \, \frac{\pi}{2}\right] ,$$

or

$$1 = \frac{4}{\pi} \sum_{k=0}^{\infty} (2k+1)^{-1} \, (-1)^k$$

so that

$$\sum_{k=0}^{\infty} (2k+1)^{-1} \, (-1)^k = \frac{\pi}{4} .$$

Let $g(x)$ be a function defined for $a \le x \le b$, and let $x_0 (a < x_0 < b)$ be a point in the interior of this interval. We define[1]

(1)
$$g(x_0 +) = \lim_{x \to x_0+} g(x) ,$$

$$g(x_0 -) = \lim_{x \to x_0-} g(x) ,$$

if these limits exist. If $g(x)$ is continuous at x_0, both $g(x_0 +)$ and $g(x_0 -)$ exist and are equal to $g(x_0)$. However $g(x_0 +)$ and $g(x_0 -)$ may be defined even at a point at which $g(x)$ is discontinuous. For example, if $s(x)$ is defined as in Sec. 1,

[1] $\lim_{x \to x_0+} g(x) = a$ means that given any $\epsilon > 0$ there exists a $\delta > 0$ such that if $x_0 < x < x_0 + \delta$, then $|g(x) - a| < \epsilon$. Note that only values of x to the right of x_0 are considered.

then $s(x)$ is discontinuous for $x = \pi$, but $s(\pi -) = 1$, $s(\pi +) = -1$. Assume now that the limits (1) exist. We further define

$$g'_r(x_0) = \lim_{h \to 0 +} \frac{g(x_0 + h) - g(x_0 +)}{h},$$

$$g'_l(x_0) = \lim_{h \to 0 -} \frac{g(x_0 + h) - g(x_0 -)}{h},$$

if, of course, these limits exist, where $g'_r(x_0)$ is called the right-hand derivative of g at x_0 and $g'_l(x_0)$ is the left-hand derivative. For example,

$$s'_r(\pi) = s'_l(\pi) = 0.$$

An argument only slightly different from that used to prove Theorem 5b suffices to prove the following result.

THEOREM 5c. If

1. $f(x) \in \mathfrak{F}$,
2. $S_N(x)$ is defined as in Sec. 3,
3. $f'_r(x_0)$ and $f'_l(x_0)$ exist,

then
$$\lim_{n \to \infty} S_N(x_0) = \tfrac{1}{2}[f(x_0 +) + f(x_0 -)].$$

The proof of Theorem 5c is left to the reader as a problem. Although much more general theorems can be given, Theorem 5c is sufficient for almost all practical purposes.

EXAMPLE 2. Discuss the convergence of the Fourier series of $t(x)$ at $x = \pi$. Clearly $t(\pi +) = t(\pi -) = 0$, and $t'_r(\pi) = 1$, $t'_l(\pi) = -1$. By Theorem 5c the Fourier series of $t(x)$ converges to 0 for $x = \pi$; that is,

$$\frac{\pi}{2} - \frac{4}{\pi} \sum_{n=0}^{\infty} (2n + 1)^{-2} = 0.$$

This is equivalent to

$$\sum_{n=0}^{\infty} (2n + 1)^{-2} = \frac{\pi^2}{8},$$

which we have already seen to be true.

PROBLEMS

1. Show by examining the Fourier series of Exercise 2 of Sec. 2 at $x = \pi$ that if $0 < c < 1$, then

$$\operatorname{ctn} c\pi = \frac{1}{\pi c} - \frac{1}{\pi} \sum_{n=1}^{\infty} \frac{2c}{n^2 - c^2}.$$

2. Evaluate the sum

$$\frac{1}{1^2} - \frac{1}{3^2} - \frac{1}{5^2} + \frac{1}{7^2} + \frac{1}{9^2} - \frac{1}{11^2} - \frac{1}{13^2} + \cdots .$$

HINT. Consider the Fourier series of $t(x)$ for an appropriately chosen value of x.

3. Show that if $f \in \mathfrak{F}$ and if $f'_r(x_0)$ and $f'_l(x_0)$ exist, then [even if $f(x)$ is not continuous at x_0] the function $\psi(u)$ which is defined as

$$\frac{f(x_0 + u) + f(x_0 - u) - f(x_0 +) - f(x_0 -)}{2 \sin (u/2)}$$

if $u \neq 0$ and as

$$f'_r(x_0) - f'_l(x_0)$$

if $u = 0$ is piecewise continuous for $-\pi \leq u \leq \pi$.

4. Prove that if $f \in \mathfrak{F}$ and if $S_N(x)$ is defined as in Sec. 3, then for any a

$$S_N(x) - a = \frac{1}{2\pi} \int_{-\pi}^{\pi} [f(x + u) + f(x - u) - 2a] D_N(u) \, du .$$

5. Using Problems 3 and 4, prove Theorem 5c.

A function $\phi(u)$ defined in an interval I including the point x_0 in its interior is said to satisfy a Lipschitz condition of order α $(0 < \alpha \leq 1)$ at x_0 if there exists a constant A such that $|\phi(x_0) - \phi(x)| \leq A |x_0 - x|^\alpha$ for $x \in I$. A function satisfying a Lipschitz condition of order α at x_0 is, of course, necessarily continuous at x_0, but it need not be differentiable. For example, the function $\phi(x) = |x|^{1/2}$ satisfies a Lipschitz condition of order $\frac{1}{2}$ at $x = 0$, but $\phi'(x)$ is not defined for $x = 0$.

6. Prove that if $\phi(u)$ is a piecewise continuous function defined in an interval containing 0 in its interior and if $\phi(u)$ satisfies a Lipschitz condition of order $\alpha(0 < \alpha \leq 1)$ at $u = 0$, then given $\epsilon > 0$ we can find a $\delta > 0$ such that

(2) $$\int_{-\delta}^{\delta} |\phi(u) D_N (u)| \, du < \epsilon \qquad (N = 0, 1, \cdots) .$$

HINT: since $|\sin (N + \frac{1}{2}) u| \leq 1$ and $|\sin u/2| \geq |u|/\pi$ for $|u| \leq \pi$ we have $|D_N (u)| \leq \pi / |u|$.

7. Use the result of Problem 6 to show that if $f \in \mathfrak{F}$ and if f satisfies a Lipschitz condition of order α at a point x_0, then $\lim\limits_{N \to \infty} S_N(x_0) = f(x_0)$. HINT: By Theorem 4c we have

$$R_N(x_0) = \frac{1}{\pi} \int_{-\pi}^{\pi} \phi(u) D_N(u) \, du$$

where $\phi(u) = f(x_0 - u) - f(x_0)$.

Given $\epsilon > 0$, pick $\delta > 0$ so that **(2)** is satisfied and let $R_N(x_0) = I_1(N) + I_2(N)$ where

$$I_1(N) = \frac{1}{\pi} \int_{|u| \leq \delta} \phi(u) \, D_N(u) \, du, \qquad I_2(N) = \frac{1}{\pi} \int_{\delta \leq |u| \leq \pi} \phi(u) \, D_N(u) \, du .$$

By construction $|I_1(N)| < \epsilon$ for $N = 0, 1, \cdots$. Next prove using Corollary 3b that there is an index N_0 such that $|I_2(N)| < \epsilon$ if $N \geq N_0$, etc.

The above result shows that the differentiabilityc ondition of Theorems 5b and 5c is much stronger than is really necessary. On the other hand it is possible to construct a function $f \in \mathfrak{F}$ which is continuous at x_0 but such that the Fourier series of f does not converge at x_0.

6. Sine and Cosine Series

In this section we shall deal with some series expansions which are closely related to the general Fourier series we have studied in previous sections.

DEFINITION 6a. Let \mathfrak{D} be the class of functions $f(x)$ defined on $0 \leq x \leq \pi$ which are piecewise continuous.

Given a function $f(x) \in \mathfrak{D}$, we associate with it a function $f_1(x) \in \mathfrak{F}$ defined as follows. We first define f_1 on $-\pi \leq x < \pi$

$$f_1(x) = \begin{cases} f(x) & (0 \leq x \leq \pi) \\ f(-x) & (-\pi \leq x < 0) \end{cases}$$

and then extend f_1 to the whole real axis by periodicity (Fig. 10)

$$f_1(x) = f_1(x + 2\pi).$$

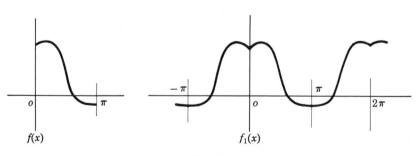

$f(x)$ $f_1(x)$

FIG. 10

Since $f_1 \in \mathfrak{F}$, we may expand it in a Fourier series

$$f_1(x) \sim \frac{a_0}{2} + \sum_{n=1}^{\infty} a_n \cos nx + b_n \sin nx$$

where

$$a_n = \frac{1}{\pi} \int_{-\pi}^{\pi} f_1(x) \cos nx \qquad (n = 0, 1, \cdots),$$

$$b_n = \frac{1}{\pi} \int_{-\pi}^{\pi} f_1(x) \sin nx \qquad (n = 1, 2, \cdots),$$

Since f_1 is even (by construction), the b_n's are all zero, and

$$a_n = \frac{2}{\pi} \int_0^{\pi} f_1(x) \cos nx \; dx$$

$$= \frac{2}{\pi} \int_0^{\pi} f(x) \cos nx \; dx \, .$$

Referring back to Theorem 5b, we see that we have proved the following result:

THEOREM 6b. If

1. $f(x) \in \mathfrak{D}$,

2. $a_n = \dfrac{2}{\pi} \displaystyle\int_0^{\pi} f(x) \cos x \; dx \quad (n = 0, 1, 2, \cdots),$

then

(1) $$\frac{a_0}{2} + \sum_{n=1}^{\infty} a_n \cos nx = f(x)$$

if $0 < x < \pi$ and $f'(x)$ exists.

Similarly if $f(x) \in \mathfrak{D}$ and if we define

$$f_2(x) = \begin{cases} f(x) & (0 < x \leq \pi) \\ 0 & (x = 0) \\ -f(-x) & (-\pi < x < 0) \end{cases}$$

and if we extend $f_2(x)$ to the whole real axis by periodicity, $f_2(x + 2\pi) = f_2(x)$, then $f_2 \in \mathfrak{F}$. Arguing as before, we obtain the following result:

THEOREM 6c. If

1. $f(x) \in \mathfrak{D}$,

2. $b_n = \dfrac{2}{\pi} \displaystyle\int_0^{\pi} f(x) \sin nx \; dx \quad (n = 1, 2, \cdots)$

then

(2) $$\sum_{n=1}^{\infty} b_n \sin nx = f(x)$$

if $0 < x < \pi$ and $f'(x)$ exists.

The series (1) is called the Fourier cosine series of $f(x)$ and the series (2) the Fourier sine series of $f(x)$.

EXAMPLE 1. Compute the cosine and sine series of the function $f(x) = x$ $(0 \leq x \leq \pi)$. We have

$$a_n = \frac{2}{\pi} \int_0^\pi x \cos nx \, dx \,.$$

If $n = 0$, then $a_0 = \pi$. If $n > 0$, then

$$a_n = \left[\frac{2}{\pi n} x \sin nx \right]_0^\pi - \frac{2}{\pi n} \int_0^\pi \sin nx \, dx$$

$$= \frac{2}{\pi n^2} \left[\cos nx \right]_0^\pi = -\frac{4}{\pi n^2} \quad \text{or} \quad 0 \quad \text{as } n \text{ is odd or even.}$$

Thus the cosine series of x is

(3) $\dfrac{\pi}{2} - \dfrac{4}{\pi} \cos x - \dfrac{4}{9\pi} \cos 3x - \dfrac{4}{25\pi} \cos 5x + \cdots \,.$

On the other hand

$$b_n = \frac{2}{\pi} \int_0^\pi x \sin nx \, dx$$

$$= -\frac{2}{\pi n} \left[x \cos nx \right]_0^\pi + \frac{2}{n} \int_0^\pi \cos nx \, dx$$

$$= -\frac{2}{n} (-1)^n \,.$$

Thus the sine series of x is

(4) $2\{\sin x - \tfrac{1}{2} \sin 2x + \tfrac{1}{3} \sin 3x + \cdots\} \,.$

The series (3) and (4) *both* converge to x for $0 < x < \pi$.

For the behavior of sine and cosine series at $x = 0$ and $x = \pi$ see Problem 5.

PROBLEMS

Expand the following functions in both cosine series and sine series.

1. $f(x) = 1$ $(0 \leq x \leq \pi)$

2. $f(x) = \cos x$ $(0 \leq x \leq \pi)$.

3. $f(x) = \sin x$ $(0 \leq x \leq \pi)$.

4. $f(x) = \sin^2 x$ $(0 \leq x \leq \pi)$.

5. Use Theorem 5c to show that if $f(x) \in \mathfrak{D}$, then the cosine series of $f(x)$:
(a) converges for $x = 0$ to $f(0 +)$ if $f_r'(0)$ exists;
(b) converges for $x = \pi$ to $f(\pi -)$ if $f_l'(\pi)$ exists.
Moreover the sine series of $f(x)$
(c) converges for $x = 0$ and $x = \pi$ to 0.

7. Complex Fourier Series

In the present section we assume familiarity with the basic properties of complex numbers. Every complex number has the form

$$a = a_1 + ia_2 \qquad (i = \sqrt{-1})$$

where a_1 and a_2 are real. a_1 is the real, and a_2 the imaginary part of a,

$$a_1 = \text{Rl } a, \qquad a_2 = \text{Im } a.$$

The complex conjugate a^* of a is given by the formula

$$a^* = a_1 - ia_2,$$

and the operation "*" has the properties

$$(a + b)^* = a^* + b^*, \qquad (ab)^* = a^* \, b^*.$$

The absolute value $|a|$ of a is defined by

$$|a| = \sqrt{a_1^2 + a_2^2} = \sqrt{aa^*}\,.$$

If $f(x)$ is a complex valued function of the *real* variable x, then $f(x)$ is defined to be continuous at x_0 if $f_1(x) = \text{Rl } f(x)$ and $f_2(x) = \text{Im } f(x)$ are both continuous at x_0 and $f(x)$ is differentiable at x_0 if $f_1(x)$ and $f_2(x)$ are both differentiable at x_0, and then

$$f'(x) = f_1'(x) + i f_2'(x)\,.$$

Similarly

$$\int_r^s f(x)\,dx = \int_r^s f_1(x)\,dx + i \int_r^s f_2(x)\,dx$$

if the two integrals on the right exist. From these definitions it can be checked that all the usual rules of the integral and differential calculus remain valid.

Let \mathfrak{F}^c be the set of all complex valued functions $f(x)$ defined on $-\infty < x < \infty$ and such that if $f_1(x) = \text{Rl } f(x)$, $f_2(x) = \text{Im } f(x)$, then f_1 and $f_2 \in \mathfrak{F}$.

We define

$$e(x) = \cos x + i \sin x \qquad (-\infty < x < \infty).$$

The following identity is easily verified

(1) $$e(x_1 \, x_2) = e(x_1)\, e(x_2).$$

We also note that

(2) $$e(x)^* = e(-x).$$

LEMMA 7a. If m and n are integers, then

$$\frac{1}{2\pi} \int_{-\pi}^{\pi} e(nx)\, [e(mx)]^* \, dx = \begin{cases} 1 & (m = n) \\ 0 & (m \neq n) . \end{cases}$$

Proof. Using (1) and (2), we see that

$$e(nx)\, [e(mx)]^* = e[(n - m)\, x]$$

$$= \cos [(n - m)\, x] + i \sin[(n - m)\, x], \text{ etc.}$$

The functions $e(nx)\,(-\infty < n < \infty)$ belong to \mathfrak{F}^c. It is natural to hope that any function $f \in \mathfrak{F}^c$ can be expressed as an infinite series of the form

(3) $$f(x) = \sum_{n=-\infty}^{\infty} c_n\, e(nx) .$$

For this to be possible it is necessary that the constants $c_0,\ c_{-1},\ c_1,\ c_{-2},\ c_2,\ \cdots ,$ be correctly chosen. In order to guess what this correct choice is, multiply both sides of (3) by $e(mx)^*$ and integrate term by term (as if the infinite sum were a finite sum). Using Lemma 7a, we obtain (after dividing by 2π)

(4) $$\frac{1}{2\pi} \int_{-\pi}^{\pi} f(x)\, [e(mx)]^* \, dx = c_m .$$

This result suggests the following definition.

DEFINITION 7b. Let $f(x) \in \mathfrak{F}^c$. If the constants $c_n(-\infty < n < \infty)$ are computed from the formula (4), then

(5) $$\sum_{-\infty}^{\infty} c_n\, e(nx)$$

is called the "complex Fourier series" of $f(x)$.

We indicate the relation between $f(x)$ and the series (5) by writing

$$f(x) \sim \sum_{-\infty}^{\infty} c_n\, e(nx) .$$

Complex Fourier series are often used, and they have some advantage particularly for theoretical purposes. The theory of complex Fourier series can be developed either by using arguments which are parallel to the arguments used for real Fourier series in Sec. 1–5 of the present chapter or by suitably applying earlier results translated into complex form. We shall use both of these procedures.

THEOREM 7c. (Bessel's inequality.) If

1. $f(x) \in \mathfrak{F}^c$,

2. $f(x) \sim \sum_{-\infty}^{\infty} c_n\, e(nx)$,

then

(6)
$$\sum_{-\infty}^{\infty} |c_n|^2 \le \frac{1}{2\pi} \int_{-\pi}^{\pi} |f(x)|^2 \, dx \,.$$

Proof. We parallel the argument used to prove Theorem 3a. We shall start the proof only, the completion being left as a problem. Let

$$S_N(x) = \sum_{n=-N}^{N} c_n \, e(nx) \,.$$

We assert that if $\psi_N(x)$ is any (complex) trigonometric polynomial of order N, that is, if ψ_N is of the form

$$\psi_N(x) = \sum_{n=-N}^{N} d_n \, e(nx)$$

where the constants d_{-N}, \cdots, d_N are any complex numbers, then

$$\frac{1}{2\pi} \int_{-\pi}^{\pi} [f(x) - S_N(x)][\,\psi_N(x)]^* \, dx = 0, \text{ etc.}$$

THEOREM 7d. If

1. $f(x) \in \mathfrak{F}^c$,

2. $f \sim \sum_{-\infty}^{\infty} c_n \, e(nx)$,

3. $S_N(x) = \sum_{-N}^{N} c_n e(nx)$,

4. $f'(x_0)$ exists,

then $\lim_{N\to\infty} S_N(x_0) = f(x_0)$.

Proof. In this case we shall obtain our proof by a suitable application of Theorem 5b. We have

$$S_N(x) = \sum_{-N}^{N} e(nx) \frac{1}{2\pi} \int_{-\pi}^{\pi} f(t) \, [e(nt)]^* \, dt$$

$$= \frac{1}{2\pi} \int_{-\pi}^{\pi} f(t) \left\{ \sum_{-N}^{N} e[n(x-t)] \right\} dt \,.$$

We assert that

(7)
$$\frac{1}{2\pi} \sum_{-N}^{N} e(nx) = \frac{1}{\pi} \frac{\sin(N+\frac{1}{2})x}{2 \sin(x/2)} \,.$$

Assuming this, we see that if $f(t) = f_1(t) + if_2(t)$ is the decomposition of $f(t)$ into its real and imaginary parts, then $S_N(x) = I_1(N) + iI_2(N)$ where

$$I_1(N) = \frac{1}{\pi} \int_{-\pi}^{\pi} f_1(t) \frac{\sin(N + \frac{1}{2})(x - t)}{2 \sin \frac{1}{2}(x - t)} dt ,$$

$$I_2(N) = \frac{1}{\pi} \int_{-\pi}^{\pi} f_2(t) \frac{\sin(N + \frac{1}{2})(x - t) dt}{2 \sin \frac{1}{2}(x - t)} .$$

Now Assumption 4 means by definition that $f_1'(x_0)$ and $f_2'(x_0)$ exist. Thus by Theorem 5b (x being set equal to x_0) we have

$$\lim_{N \to \infty} I_1(N) = f_1(x_0), \qquad \lim_{N \to \infty} I_2(N) = f_2(x_0), \text{ etc.}$$

EXAMPLE 1. Compute the complex Fourier coefficients of the function $f(x)$ which is defined as x for $-\pi \leq x < \pi$ and is then extended to the whole real axis using $f(x + 2\pi) = f(x)$. We have, if $n \neq 0$,

$$c_n = \frac{1}{2\pi} \int_{-\pi}^{\pi} x \, e(-nx) \, dx$$

$$= \frac{1}{2\pi} \left[x \frac{e(-nx)}{-in} \right]_{-\pi}^{\pi} - \frac{1}{2\pi} \int_{-\pi}^{\pi} \frac{e(-nx)}{-in} dx$$

$$= \frac{1}{2\pi} \left[x \frac{e(-nx)}{-in} \right]_{-\pi}^{\pi} - \frac{1}{2\pi} \left[\frac{e(-nx)}{-n^2} \right]_{-\pi}^{\pi} .$$

Since $c_0 = 0$, as is easily seen, we find that

$$c_n = \begin{cases} \dfrac{(-1)^{n-1}}{in} & (n \neq 0) \\ 0 & (n = 0) . \end{cases}$$

PROBLEMS

1. Compute the complex Fourier series of the function $s(x)$ of Sec. 1.

2. Compute the complex Fourier series of the function $f(x)$ which is equal to $e(\alpha x)$ for $-\pi \leq x < \pi$ and is then extended to the whole real axis by periodicity, $f(x) = f(x + 2\pi)$. Here $0 < \alpha < 1$.

3. Compute the complex Fourier series of the function $t(x)$ of Sec. 1.

4. Prove Formula (**7**).

5. Complete the proof of Theorem 7c.

6. Prove that if $f \in \mathfrak{F}^c$ and if $f(x) \sim \sum\limits_{n=-\infty}^{\infty} c_n \, e(nx)$, then for any real constant a,

$$f(x - a) \sim \sum_{n=-\infty}^{\infty} c_n \, e(-na) \, e(nx).$$

7. Prove that if $f \in \mathfrak{F}^c$ and if $f_1(x) = f(-x)^*$, then

$$f_1(x) \sim \sum_{n=-\infty}^{\infty} c_n^* \, e(nx).$$

[4]

Uniform Convergence

1. Sequences of Functions

Let us consider a sequence the terms of which are continuous functions of x, where x belongs to the finite interval $I = \{a \leq x \leq b\}$,

$$u_1(x),\ u_2(x),\ u_3(x),\ \cdots.$$

This is, of course, not one sequence but rather a family of sequences, one sequence for each assignment of the variable x. Let us assume that for each $x \in I$, $\lim_{k \to \infty} u_k(x) = u(x)$ exists. It is now rather natural to ask if under these assumptions we shall always have

(1) $$\lim_{k \to \infty} \int_a^b u_k(x)\, dx = \int_a^b u(x)\, dx.$$

The answer is no. A first difficulty is that $u(x)$ although the limit of a sequence of continuous functions may not be continuous or even Riemann integrable.

EXAMPLE 1. Let

$$s_k(x) = x^k(1 + x^k)^{-1} \qquad (k = 1, 2, \cdots), \qquad I = \{0 \leq x \leq 2\}.$$

Then $\lim_{k \to \infty} s_k(x) = s(x)$, where $s(x)$ is 0 for $0 \leq x < 1$, is $\frac{1}{2}$ for $x = 1$, and is 1 for $1 < x \leq 2$; $s(x)$ is thus discontinuous at $x = 1$.

The function $s(x)$ of Example 1 although discontinuous is Riemann integrable. It is possible to construct a sequence of functions continuous on $I = \{0 \leq x \leq 1\}$ which converges for all $x \in I$ to a (bounded) function which is so discontinuous that it is not Riemann integrable. However this construction is too complicated to be included here.

To avoid this difficulty, let us now make the additional assumption that $s(x)$ is continuous. The following example shows that **(1)** may still not hold true.

EXAMPLE 2. Let $I = \{0 \leq x \leq 1\}$, and let

$$t_k(x) = (k + 1)(k + 2)x(1 - x)^k \qquad (k = 1, 2, \cdots).$$

Then $\lim\limits_{k\to\infty} t_k(x) = t(x)$ where $t(x)$ is 0 for $0 \le \dot{x} \le 1$. Integrating by parts, we find that

$$\int_0^1 t_k(x)\, dx = 1 \qquad (k = 1, 2, \cdots)$$

and hence $\lim\limits_{k\to\infty} \int_0^1 t_k(x)\, dx = 1$. On the other hand $\int_0^1 t(x)\, dx = 0$. It is instructive to examine the graphs of the functions $t_k(x)$ (Fig. 11.)

Our original question must now be replaced by another. What additional conditions imposed on the sequence $\{u_k(x)\}_1^\infty$ will ensure the validity of (1)? In this chapter we shall, among other things, find convenient sufficient conditions for (1) to hold. The principal tool in carrying out this program is the concept of uniform convergence.

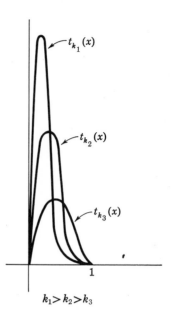

$k_1 > k_2 > k_3$

Fig. 11

DEFINITION 1a. Let S be a subset of the real numbers and for each k $(k = 1, 2, \cdots)$; let $u_k(x)$ be a function (not necessarily continuous) defined on S. We assume that for each $x \in S$ the sequence $\{u_k(x)\}_1^\infty$ is convergent, and we set $u(x) = \lim\limits_{k\to\infty} u_k(x)$. The sequence $\{u_k(x)\}_1^\infty$ is said to converge *uniformly* on S if for each $\epsilon > 0$ there exists an integer N such that

$$(2) \qquad\qquad\qquad | u(x) - u_k(x) | < \epsilon$$

for $k \ge N$ and all $x \in S$.

Note that although it follows from the assumption of convergence that for *each* $x \in S$, given $\epsilon > 0$ there exists an integer $N(x)$, depending on x, such that $| u(x) - u_k(x) | < \epsilon$ if $k \ge N(x)$, it does not follow that there will exist *one* integer N such that (2) will hold for *all* $x \in S$ if $k \ge N$.

EXAMPLE 3. The sequence $u_k(x) = (1 - x^{k+1})/(1 - x)$ $(k = 1, 2, \cdots)$ converges uniformly to $u(x) = 1/(1 - x)$ on the set $S = \{|x| \le a\}$ if $0 < a < 1$. To see this, we note that

$$| u(x) - u_k(x) | = \frac{| x |^{k+1}}{1 - x}$$

$$\le \frac{a^{n+1}}{1 - a} \qquad \text{for } | x | \le a .$$

Given $\epsilon > 0$, if we choose N so large that

$$\frac{a^{N+1}}{1-a} < \epsilon,$$

then we shall have

$$|u(x) - u_k(x)| < \epsilon$$

for $k \geq N$ and all $x \in S$.

Let us examine the geometrical picture which corresponds to uniform convergence. Suppose that $\lim\limits_{k \to \infty} t_k(x) = t(x)$ uniformly on $a \leq x \leq b$. Then by the definition of uniform convergence, given $\epsilon > 0$ there is an N such that if $k \geq N$, $|t_k(x) - t(x)| < \epsilon$ for $a \leq x \leq b$, or equivalently if $k \geq N$ and $a \leq x \leq b$, $t(x) - \epsilon < t_k(x) < t(x) + \epsilon$. This means that if $k \geq N$, then $t_k(x)$ lies for $a \leq x \leq b$ within the band whose upper and lower boundaries are $y = t(x) + \epsilon$ and $y = t(x) - \epsilon$. (Fig. 12.)

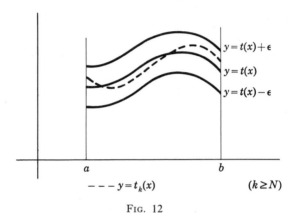

$$y = t(x) + \epsilon$$
$$y = t(x)$$
$$y = t(x) - \epsilon$$

$a \qquad\qquad\qquad b$

$- - - y = t_k(x) \qquad\qquad (k \geq N)$

FIG. 12

We shall now show that the sequences in Examples 1 and 2 do not converge uniformly. If in Example 1, $s_k(x)$ converged uniformly to $s(x)$, then for any small positive ϵ $s_k(x)$ must be in the strip $s(x) - \epsilon < y < s(x) + \epsilon$ $(0 \leq x \leq 2)$ for all sufficiently large k. But since this strip is discontinuous and $s_k(x)$ is continuous, this is impossible (Fig. 13.)

$o \qquad\qquad\qquad 2$

FIG. 13

If in Example 2, $t_k(x)$ converged uniformly to $t(x) = 0$ $(0 \le x \le 1)$, then for any ϵ and all sufficiently large k we would have $|t_k(x)| < \epsilon$ $(0 \le x \le 1)$. It is easily seen that for fixed k, $t_k(x)$ attains its maximum value in $0 \le x \le 1$ for $x = 1/(k+1)$. We have

$$t_k\left(\frac{1}{k+1}\right) = (k+2)\left(1 + \frac{1}{k}\right)^{-k}.$$

Since $\lim_{k \to \infty} (1 + 1/k)^{-k} = e^{-1}$, it follows that $t_k[1/(k+1)]$ increases beyond all bounds as k increases and thus $|t_k(x)| < \epsilon$ $(0 \le x \le 1)$ fails for all sufficiently large k.

The results of Sec. 1 of Chapter 1 have (modified) analogues for uniform convergence. Note that in the following theorems S is any subset of the real numbers and the $s_n(x)$'s are not assumed to be continuous.

THEOREM 1b. If $\lim_{n \to \infty} s_n(x) = s(x)$ uniformly for $x \in S$, then $\lim_{n \to \infty} c s_n(x) = c s(x)$ uniformly for $x \in S$.

THEOREM 1c. If $\lim_{n \to \infty} s_n(x) = s(x)$ and if $\lim_{n \to \infty} t_n(x) = t(x)$, both uniformly for $x \in S$, then $\lim_{n \to \infty} s_n(x) + t_n(x) = s(x) + t(x)$ uniformly for $x \in S$.

THEOREM 1d. If

1. $\lim_{n \to \infty} s_n(x) = s(x)$ uniformly for $x \in S$,

2. $\lim_{n \to \infty} t_n(x) = t(x)$ uniformly for $x \in S$,

3. there is a constant M such that $|s(x)| \le M$ for $x \in S$ and $|t(x)| \le M$ for $x \in S$,

then $\lim_{n \to \infty} s_n(x) t_n(x) = s(x) t(x)$ uniformly for $x \in S$.

THEOREM 1e. If

1. $\lim_{n \to \infty} s_n(x) = s(x)$ uniformly for $x \in S$,

2. there is a constant $m > 0$ such that $|s(x)| \ge m$ for $x \in S$,

then $$\lim_{n \to \infty} \frac{1}{s_n(x)} = \frac{1}{s(x)}$$ uniformly for $x \in S$.

We shall prove only Theorem 1d; the remaining proofs are left as problems.

Proof of Theorem 1d. Take $\epsilon = 1$; then there is an integer N_1 such that if $k \ge N_1$, then $|s_k(x) - M| \le 1$ for $x \in S$. Thus if $k \ge N_1$,

$$|s_k(x)| \le M + 1 \quad (x \in S).$$

Let an arbitrary $\epsilon > 0$ be given. There are integers N_2 and N_3 such that if $k \ge N_2$,

$$|s_k(x) - s(x)| < \frac{\epsilon}{2M + 1} \quad (x \in S)$$

and if $k \geq N_3$,

$$| t_k(x) - t(x) | < \frac{\epsilon}{2M + 1} \qquad x \in S.$$

Let $N = \max\{N_1, N_2, N_3\}$. We assert that if $k \geq N$, then

$$| s(x)\, t(x) - s_k(x)\, t_k(x) | < \epsilon \qquad \text{for } x \in S.$$

We have

$$s(x)\, t(x) - s_k(x)\, t_k(x) = s(x)\, t(x) - s_k(x)\, t(x)$$
$$+ s_k(x)\, t(x) - s_k(x)\, t_k(x)$$
$$| s(x)\, t(x) - s_k(x)\, t_k(x) | \leq | t(x) | \cdot | s(x) - s_k(x) |$$
$$+ | s_k(x) | \cdot | t(x) - t_k(x) |$$
$$< M \cdot \frac{\epsilon}{2M + 1} + (M + 1) \cdot \frac{\epsilon}{2M + 1} = \epsilon,$$

as desired.

PROBLEMS

1. Let $s_k(x) = \cos (x/k)$; then $\lim\limits_{k \to \infty} s_k(x) = 1$ for $-\infty < x < \infty$. Show that the convergence is uniform on $\{| x | \leq a\}$ if $a < \infty$. Is the convergence uniform on $-\infty < x < \infty$? Justify your answer.

2. Let $s_k(x) = (kx^2 + 2x + 1)/(kx + 1)$. Find $s(x) = \lim\limits_{k \to \infty} s_k(x)$ for $0 \leq x < \infty$. Is the convergence of $s_k(x)$ to $s(x)$ uniform on $\{0 \leq x \leq 1\}$? On $\{1 \leq x < \infty\}$? Justify your answers.

3. Let $s_k(x) = xke^{-kx}$. Find $s(x) = \lim\limits_{k \to \infty} s_k(x)$ for $0 \leq x < \infty$. Is the convergence uniform on $\{0 \leq x < \infty\}$? Justify your answer.

4. (a) Prove that if the sequence $\{t_k(x)\}_1^\infty$ converges uniformly for $x \in S$, it converges uniformly for $x \in T$ if $T \subset S$.
(b) Prove that if the sequence $\{t_k(x)\}_1^\infty$ converges uniformly for $x \in S_1$ and uniformly for $x \in S_2$, it converges uniformly for $x \in S = S_1 \cup S_2$.

5. Prove that if the sequence $\{t_k(x)\}_1^\infty$ converges for each $x \in S$ and if the set S consists of only finitely many points, $S = \{x_1, x_2, \cdots, x_m\}$, then $\{t_k(x)\}_1^\infty$ converges uniformly for $x \in S$.

6. Prove Theorem 1b.

7. Prove Theorem 1c.

8. Prove Theorem 1e.

9. Show that Theorem 1d is no longer true if Assumption 3 is omitted.

10. Let $s_k(x) = k \sin^2 x/(1 + k \tan x)$ $(k = 1, 2, \cdots)$. Show that $\lim_{k \to \infty} s_k(x) = \frac{1}{2} \sin 2x$ for $0 \leq x \leq \pi/4$, and prove that the convergence is uniform. HINT: Given $\epsilon > 0$, consider $\{0 \leq x \leq \epsilon\}$ and $\{\epsilon \leq x \leq \pi/4\}$ separately.

11. Show that if $s_k(x) = k^2[e^{x/k} - 1 - x/k]$ for $k = 1, 2, \cdots$, then $\lim_{k \to \infty} s_k(x) = \frac{1}{2}x^2$ for $-\infty < x < \infty$. Prove that the convergence is uniform for $\{|x| \leq a\}$ for any finite a. HINT: Use Theorem 4b of Chapter 2.

2. Uniform Convergence of Continuous Functions

The reason for the introduction of the concept of uniform convergence lies in the results of the present section.

Example 1 of Sec. 1 showed that a sequence of continuous functions on an interval $a \leq x \leq b$ can converge at each point of the interval to a limit function which may not be continuous. The following result shows that if we assume uniform convergence, this undesirable effect cannot occur.

THEOREM 2a. If the functions $s_k(x)$ $(k = 1, 2, \cdots)$ are continuous for $a \leq x \leq b$ and if $\lim_{k \to \infty} s_k(x) = s(x)$ uniformly for x in $a \leq x \leq b$, then $s(x)$ is continuous for $a \leq x \leq b$.

Proof. By the definition of continuity (see Sec. 2 of the Appendix) we must show that given $x_0(a \leq x_0 \leq b)$ and given $\epsilon > 0$, there exists a $\delta > 0$ (which may depend on x_0 and on ϵ) such that if $a \leq x \leq b$ and if $|x - x_0| < \delta$, then $|s(x_0) - s(x)| < \epsilon$. By assumption there is an integer N such that if $k \geq N$, then $|s(x) - s_k(x)| < \epsilon/3$ $(a \leq x \leq b)$. In particular

(1′)
$$|s(x) - s_N(x)| < \frac{\epsilon}{3} \quad (a \leq x \leq b).$$

Since $s_N(x)$ is continuous, there exists a $\delta > 0$ such that

(1″)
$$|s_N(x_0) - s_N(x)| < \frac{\epsilon}{3}$$

if $a \leq x \leq b$ and if $|x - x_0| < \delta$. We assert that $|s(x_0) - s(x)| < \epsilon$ if $|x - x_0| < \delta$. We have

$$s(x_0) - s(x) = s(x_0) - s_N(x_0) + s_N(x_0) - s_N(x) + s_N(x) - s(x),$$

(2) $\quad |s(x_0) - s(x)| \leq |s(x_0) - s_N(x_0)| + |s_N(x_0) - s_N(x)| + |s_N(x) - s(x)|$

$$< \frac{\epsilon}{3} + \frac{\epsilon}{3} + \frac{\epsilon}{3} = \epsilon.$$

In our estimation of the terms on the right-hand side of **(2)**, we have used **(1′)**, **(1″)**, and **(1′)**, respectively.

THEOREM 2b. If the functions $s_k(x)$ $(k = 1, 2, \cdots)$ are continuous for $a \leq x \leq b$ and if $\lim_{k \to \infty} s_k(x) = s(x)$ uniformly for $a \leq x \leq b$, then

(3)
$$\int_a^b s(x) \, dx = \lim_{k \to \infty} \int_a^b s_k(x) \, dx \, .$$

This result can also be written as

$$\int_a^b \lim_{k \to \infty} s_k(x) \, dx = \lim_{k \to \infty} \int_a^b s(x) \, dx \, .$$

Proof. By Theorem 2a the function $s(x)$ is continuous and therefore Riemann integrable. We have

$$\int_a^b s(x) \, dx - \int_a^b s_k(x) \, dx = \int_a^b [s(x) - s_k(x)] \, dx \, ,$$

from which it follows that

$$\left| \int_a^b s(x) \, dx - \int_a^b s_k(x) \, dx \right| \leq \int_a^b | s(x) - s_k(x) | \, dx$$

(see Lemma 3b of Chapter 2). By assumption, given $\epsilon > 0$, there is an integer N such that if $k \geq N$, then

$$| s(x) - s_k(x) | < \frac{\epsilon}{b - a} \qquad (a \leq x \leq b) \, .$$

By Lemma 3c of Chapter 2 if $k \geq N$, then we have

$$\int_a^b | s(x) - s_k(x) | \, dx < \int_a^b \epsilon(b - a)^{-1} \, dx = \epsilon \, ,$$

and thus

$$\left| \int_a^b s(x) \, dx - \int_a^b s_k(x) \, dx \right| < \epsilon$$

for $k \geq N$, as desired.

THEOREM 2c. If[1]

 1. $s_k(x) \in \mathfrak{C}^{(1)}$ $(a \leq x \leq b)$,

 2. $\lim_{k \to \infty} s_k(x) = s(x)$ $(a \leq x \leq b)$,

 3. $\lim_{k \to \infty} s'_k(x)$ exists uniformly for $a \leq x \leq b$,

[1] We recall that $s_k(x) \in \mathfrak{C}^{(1)}$ $a \leq x \leq b$ means that $s_k(x)$ and $s'_k(x)$ are both continuous for $a \leq x \leq b$. Similarly $u_k(x) \in \mathfrak{C}$ (in Theorem 2e) means that $u_k(x)$ is continuous for $a \leq x \leq b$.

then $s(x)$ is differentiable for $a \leq x \leq b$ and

(4)
$$\lim_{k \to \infty} \frac{d}{dx} s_k(x) = \frac{d}{dx} s(x) \qquad (a < x < b).$$

The result is true for $x = a(x = b)$ if derivative is replaced by right-hand (left-hand) derivative. Note that the conclusion can also be written as

$$\lim_{k \to \infty} \frac{d}{dx} s_k(x) = \frac{d}{dx} \lim_{k \to \infty} s_k(x) \,.$$

Proof. By Assumption 3 the sequence $\{s'_k(x)\}_1^\infty$ converges uniformly. Let us set $\sigma(x) = \lim_{k \to \infty} s'_k(x)$ $(a \leq x \leq b)$. We must prove that $s(x)$ is differentiable and that $s'(x) = \sigma(x)$. By Assumption 1 the functions $s'_k(x)$ are continuous on $a \leq x \leq b$. As the uniform limit of continuous functions $\sigma(x)$ is continuous on $a \leq x \leq b$ by Theorem 2a, and if $a < y < b$ then by Theorem 2b

$$\int_a^y \sigma(x) \, dx = \lim_{k \to \infty} \int_a^y s'_k(x) \, dx$$

(5)
$$= \lim_{k \to \infty} [s_k(y) - s_k(a)]$$

$$= s(y) - s(a) \,.$$

In this last step we have used Assumption 2. Since $\sigma(x)$ is continuous, the formula (5) implies that $s(y)$ is differentiable for $a < y < b$ and that $\sigma(y) = s'(y)$.

The principal application of these results will be to sequences of partial sums of infinite series. For the sake of convenience we restate our results in this form.

DEFINITION 2d. The infinite *series* $\sum_{k=1}^\infty u_k(x)$ $(a \leq x \leq b)$ is said to converge uniformly for $a \leq x \leq b$ if the *sequence* $s_n(x) = \sum_{k=1}^n u_k(x)$ of partial sums converges uniformly for $a \leq x \leq b$.

THEOREM 2e. If

1. $u_k(x) \in \mathfrak{C}$ $(a \leq x \leq b, \qquad k = 1, 2, \cdots)$,

2. $\sum_1^\infty u_k(x) = s(x)$ uniformly for $a \leq x \leq b$,

then $s(x)$ is continuous for $a \leq x \leq b$.

THEOREM 2f. If

1. $u_k(x) \in \mathfrak{C}$ $(a \leq x \leq b, \qquad k = 1, 2, \cdots)$,

2. $\sum_1^\infty u_k(x) = s(x)$ uniformly for $a \leq x \leq b$,

then
$$\int_a^b s(x) \, dx = \sum_{k=1}^\infty \int_a^b u_k(x) \, dx \,.$$

THEOREM 2g. If

 1. $u_k(x) \in \mathfrak{C}^{(1)}$ $(a \leq x \leq b$ $k = 1, 2, \cdots)$,

 2. $\sum_{k=1}^{\infty} u_k(x) = s(x)$ $(a \leq x \leq b)$,

 3. $\sum_{k=1}^{\infty} u_k'(x)$ converges uniformly for $a \leq x \leq b$,

then
$$\frac{d}{dx} s(x) = \sum_{k=1}^{\infty} \frac{d}{dx} u_k(x) \qquad (a < x < b).$$

In order to make use of Theorems 2f and 2g, we need efficient methods for establishing uniform convergence. The following theorem due to Weierstrass, essentially a "uniform comparison test," is the simplest method.

THEOREM 2h. Let $u_k(x)$ $(k = 1, 2, \cdots)$ be defined for $x \in S$. If for each $k = 1, 2, \cdots$,

(6) $$|\, u_k(x)\,| \leq v_k \qquad (x \in S)$$

where v_k is independent of x and if the series $\sum_{k=1}^{\infty} v_k$ is convergent, then the series

(7) $$\sum_{k=1}^{\infty} u_k(x)$$

converges uniformly (and absolutely) for $x \in S$.

Proof. Theorems 5a and 7b of Chapter 1 imply that the series (7) converges absolutely for each $x \in S$. Denoting the sum by $s(x)$ and the partial sum of order n by $s_n(x)$ we have
$$s(x) - s_n(x) = r_n(x)$$

where
$$r_n(x) = \sum_{k=n+1}^{\infty} u_k(x)\,.$$

Since
$$|\, r_n(x)\,| \leq \sum_{k=n+1}^{\infty} |\, u_k(x)\,| \leq \sum_{k=n+1}^{\infty} v_k\,,$$

it follows that if given $\epsilon > 0$ we choose $N > 0$ so large that $\sum_{N+1}^{\infty} v_k < \epsilon$, then for $n \geq N$ we must have $|\, r_n(x)\,| < \epsilon$ if $x \in S$, and thus $|\, s(x) - s_n(x)\,| < \epsilon$ $(n \geq N,\ x \in S)$, as desired.

EXAMPLE 1. Show that
$$\int_0^x e^{-t^2}\, dt = \sum_{k=0}^{\infty} \frac{(-1)^k}{k!} \frac{x^{2k+1}}{2k+1}$$

for $-\infty < x < \infty$. By Example 2 of Sec. 3 of Chapter 2 we know that
$$e^x = \sum_0^{\infty} \frac{x^k}{k!}$$

for $-\infty < x < \infty$. Setting $x = -t^2$, we obtain

$$e^{-t^2} = \sum_0^\infty \frac{(-1)^k \, t^{2k}}{k!}$$

for $-\infty < t < \infty$. Let $u_k(t) = (-1)^k \, t^{2k}/k!$. If $|t| \leq a \ (0 < a < \infty)$, then we may take $v_k = a^{2k}/k!$. We have $|u_k(t)| \leq v_k$ for $|t| \leq a$. The convergence of the series $\sum_0^\infty v_k$ may be demonstrated by means of Theorem 5e of Chapter 1. Thus by Theorem 2h the series for e^{-t^2} converges uniformly for $|t| \leq a$. Applying Theorem 2f, we obtain

$$\int_0^x e^{-t^2} \, dt = \sum_0^\infty \int_0^x \frac{(-1)^k \, t^{2k}}{k!} \, dt = \sum_0^\infty \frac{(-1)^k}{k!} \, \frac{x^{2k+1}}{2k+1}$$

if $|x| \leq a$. Since a is arbitrary, this holds for all $x \ (-\infty < x < \infty)$.

EXAMPLE 2. It has been shown (see Problems 9 and 10 of Sec. 4 Chapter 1) that the series

$$\zeta(x) = \sum_{n=1}^\infty n^{-x}$$

converges for $1 < x < \infty$. We wish to show that under the same restrictions on x

$$\frac{d}{dx} \, \zeta(x) = \sum_{n=1}^\infty - \log n \cdot n^{-x} \,.$$

To this end we employ Theorem 2g, Assumptions 1 and 2 of which are clearly satisfied. Suppose now that $1 < a \leq x < \infty$. Then $|-\log n \cdot n^{-x}| \leq \log n \cdot n^{-a}$ for $a \leq x < \infty$. The series $\sum_{n=1}^\infty \log n \cdot n^{-a}$ can be shown to be convergent by comparison with the series $\sum_{n=1}^\infty n^{-a_1}$ where $1 < a_1 < a$. Thus by Theorem 2h, Assumption 3 of Theorem 2g is satisfied, and our desired result follows.

EXAMPLE 3. We know that the function $y(x)$ defined by the series,

$$y(x) = \sum_{n=0}^\infty \frac{a^n}{n!} \, x^n \qquad (-\infty < x < \infty) \,,$$

is equal to e^{ax} and therefore $y'(x) = ae^{ax} = ay(x)$. We can however prove this directly from the series definition of $y(x)$ without using any of the properties of the exponential function. Differentiating the series for $y(x)$ formally term by term, we obtain

$$y'(x) = \sum_{n=0}^\infty \frac{a^n}{n!} \, nx^{n-1} \,.$$

Since this series is easily seen (using Theorem 2h) to converge uniformly for x

in any finite interval, our formal procedure may be justified by an appeal to Theorem 2g. We now have

$$y'(x) = \sum_{n=1}^{\infty} a \frac{a^{n-1}}{(n-1)!} x^{n-1} = a \sum_{m=0}^{\infty} \frac{a^m}{m!} x^m = ay(x),$$

as desired.

EXAMPLE 4. Expand the function

$$I(z) = \int_0^{\pi/2} \cos t (1 - z \sin^2 t)^{-1} \, dt \qquad (-\infty < z < 1)$$

as a power series in z. Since $(1 - x)^{-1} = \sum_{k=0}^{\infty} x^k$, we find on setting $x = z \sin^2 t$ that if $|z| < 1$,

$$(1 - z \sin^2 t)^{-1} = \sum_{k=0}^{\infty} z^k (\sin t)^{2k}.$$

Moreover for z fixed this series converges uniformly in t for $0 \le t \le \pi/2$, since $|z^k (\sin t)^{2k}| \le |z|^k$ for $0 \le t \le \pi/2$, $k = 0, 1, \cdots$, and $\sum_0^{\infty} |z|^k$ converges. Thus by Theorem 2f

$$I(z) = \sum_{k=0}^{\infty} z^k \int_0^{\pi/2} (\sin t)^{2k} \cos t \, dt$$

$$= \sum_{k=0}^{\infty} \frac{z^k}{2k + 1} \qquad (|z| < 1).$$

PROBLEMS

In all the following problems every step should be justified in detail.

1. Prove by integrating the geometric series and without using the results of Chapter 2 that

$$- \log(1 - x) = \sum_{k=1}^{\infty} \frac{x^k}{k} \qquad (|x| < 1).$$

2. Prove by differentiating the geometric series and without using the results of Chapter 2 that

$$(1 - x)^{-2} = \sum_{k=0}^{\infty} (-1)^k \binom{-2}{k} x^k \qquad (|x| < 1).$$

3. (a) Prove that

$$\int_0^x \frac{\sin u}{u} \, du = \sum_{n=0}^{\infty} \frac{(-1)^n x^{2n+1}}{(2n + 1)(2n + 1)!} \qquad (-\infty < x < \infty).$$

(b) Compute $\int_0^{\pi/4} (\sin u) u^{-1} \, du$ correct to two decimal places with an error of at most one unit in the second place.

4. Prove that

$$\frac{\pi}{4} = 1 - \frac{1}{3} + \frac{1}{5} - \frac{1}{7} + \cdots$$

by integrating the Maclaurin series for $(1 + x^2)^{-1}$ between appropriate limits.

5. Let the functions $s(x)$ and $c(x)$ be *defined* by the series expansions

$$s(x) = \sum_{n=0}^{\infty} \frac{(-1)^n}{(2n+1)!} x^{2n+1} \qquad (-\infty < x < x < \infty),$$

$$c(x) = \sum_{n=0}^{\infty} \frac{(-1)^n}{(2n)!} x^{2n} \qquad (-\infty < x < \infty).$$

Prove directly [without identifying $s(x)$ as sin x or $c(x)$ as cos x] that $s'(x) = c(x)$ and $c'(x) = -s(x)$.

6. Let a, b, c, be integers, and let $c > b > 0$. The hypergeometric function may be defined by the definite integral

$$F(a, b; c; x) = \frac{(c-1)!}{(b-1)!\,(c-b-1)!} \int_0^1 t^{b-1}(1-t)^{c-b-1}(1-tx)^{-a}\, dt$$

for $-\infty < x < 1$. Show that for $|x| < 1$,

$$F(a, b; c; x) = \sum_{n=0}^{\infty} \frac{(a)_n (b)_n}{(c)_n n!} x^n.$$

Here $(d)_0 = 1$, $(d)_n = d(d+1) \cdots (d+n-1)$ $(n \geq 1)$. This result is valid without the restriction that a, b, c be integers if the factorials are replaced by suitable gamma functions.

For $n = 0, 1, 2, \cdots$, let us set

$$J_n(x) = \sum_{k=0}^{\infty} \frac{(-1)^k}{k!(k+n)!} \left(\frac{x}{2}\right)^{2k+n} \qquad (-\infty < x < \infty).$$

It is easily verified, using Theorem 5e of Chapter 1, that each of the above series converges for $-\infty < x < \infty$. $J_n(x)$ is the Bessel function of index or order n. Bessel functions are of great importance in many mathematical investigations.

7. (a) Prove that $\dfrac{d}{dx}[x^n J_n(x)] = x^n J_{n-1}(x)$ for $n = 1, 2, \cdots$.

(b) Prove that $\dfrac{d}{dx}[x^{-n} J_n(x)] = -x^{-n} J_{n+1}(x)$ for $n = 0, 1, \cdots$.

8. Deduce from the formulas of Problem 7 that

$$x^2 J_n''(x) + x J_n'(x) + (x^2 - n^2) J_n(x) = 0 \qquad (n = 0, 1, \cdots).$$

HINT: Consider

$$\left\{ x^{-n-1} \frac{d}{dx} x^{n+1} \right\} \left\{ x^n \frac{d}{dx} x^{-n} \right\} J_n(x) .$$

9. Prove that for $-\infty < x < \infty$ and $n = 0, 1, \cdots$,

$$\int_0^{\pi/2} \cos (x \sin \phi) (\cos \phi)^{2n} \, d\phi = \sum_{k=0}^{\infty} \frac{(-1)^k x^{2k}}{(2k)!} \int_0^{\pi/2} (\sin \phi)^{2k} (\cos \phi)^{2n} \, d\phi .$$

10. (a) Prove by induction on k or otherwise that

$$\int_0^{\pi/2} (\sin \phi)^{2k} \, d\phi = \frac{\pi (2k)!}{2^{2k+1} (k!)^2} \qquad (k = 0, 1, \cdots) .$$

(b) Prove by induction on n (using Part a) that

$$\int_0^{\pi/2} (\sin \phi)^{2k} (\cos \phi)^{2n} \, d\phi = \frac{\pi (2k)! \, (2n)!}{2^{2k+2n+1} \, n! k! (n + k)!} \qquad (n = 0, 1, \cdots).$$

11. Using the results of Problems 9 and 10, show that for $-\infty < x < \infty$,

$$J_n(x) = \frac{2^{n+1} \, n!}{\pi (2n)!} \left(\frac{x}{2} \right)^n \int_0^{\pi/2} \cos(x \sin \phi) (\cos \phi)^{2n} \, d\phi .$$

12. Let $J_n(z)$ be defined for $n < 0$ by

$$J_{-n}(z) = (-1)^n J_n(z) \qquad (n = 1, 2, \cdots) .$$

Prove that

$$\frac{1}{2\pi} \int_{-\pi}^{\pi} e(z \sin \phi) \, e(n \phi)^* \, d\phi = J_n(z) \qquad (-\infty < n < \infty).$$

Here $e(x) = \cos x + i \sin x$.

12. It was shown in Problem 1 of Sec. 5 of Chapter 3 that if $0 < a < \pi$, then

$$\operatorname{ctn} a - \frac{1}{a} = \sum_{k=1}^{\infty} \frac{-2a}{k^2 \pi^2 - a^2} .$$

Show that if $\epsilon > 0$, this series converges uniformly for $U \le |a| \le \pi - \epsilon$.

13. (a) Use the result of Problem 12 to prove that if $0 \le x < \pi$, then

$$\log \sin x - \log x = \sum_{k=1}^{\infty} \log\left(1 - \frac{x^2}{k^2 \pi^2} \right) .$$

(b) Let us make the definitions

$$\prod_1^n a_k = a_1 a_2 \cdots a_n ,$$

$$\prod_1^\infty a_k = \lim_{n \to \infty} \prod_1^n a_k .$$

Show that with this notation if $0 \leq x < \pi$, then

$$\sin x = x \prod_{k=1}^{\infty} \left(1 - \frac{x^2}{k^2\pi^2}\right).$$

(It is easily shown on the basis of what we have already done that this formula is in fact valid for $-\infty < x < \infty$. However we omit this.)

3. Miscellaneous Results

If in Theorem 1d we consider the case where S is a finite closed interval $a \leq x \leq b$ and where the functions $\{s_n(x)\}_1^{\infty}$ and $\{t_n(x)\}_1^{\infty}$ are continuous, then as we shall show, Assumption 3 is a consequence of Assumptions 1 and 2 and can therefore be omitted.

THEOREM 3a. If

1. $s_n(x) \in \mathfrak{C}$ $(a \leq x \leq b, \quad n = 1, 2, \cdots)$,
2. $\lim_{n\to\infty} s_n(x) = s(x)$ uniformly on $a \leq x \leq b$,
3. $t_n(x) \in \mathfrak{C}$ $(a \leq x \leq b, \quad n = 1, 2, \cdots)$,
4. $\lim_{n\to\infty} t_n(x) = t(x)$ uniformly on $a \leq x \leq b$,

then $\lim_{n\to\infty} s_n(x) t_n(x) = s(x) t(x)$ uniformly for $a \leq x \leq b$.

Proof. By Theorem 2a, $s(x)$ and $t(x)$ are continuous for $a \leq x \leq b$. It follows by Theorem 2c of the Appendix that there is a constant M_1 such that $|s(x)| \leq M_1$ for $a \leq x \leq b$. Similarly there is a constant M_2 such that $|t(x)| \leq M_2$ for $a \leq x \leq b$. If we set $M = \max\{M_1, M_2\}$, all the assumptions of Theorem 1d are satisfied, and applying Theorem 1d, we obtain our desired result.

THEOREM 3b. If

1. $s_n(x) \in \mathfrak{C}$ $(a \leq x \leq b, \quad n = 1, 2. \cdots)$,
2. $\lim_{n\to\infty} s_n(x) = s(x)$ uniformly $a \leq x \leq b$,
3. $s(x) \neq 0$ for $a \leq x \leq b$,

then $\lim_{n\to\infty} \dfrac{1}{s_n(x)} = \dfrac{1}{s(x)}$ uniformly for $a \leq x \leq b$.

The proof of this result is left as an exercise.

Before going on, the reader should ask himself if Theorems 3a and 3b remain true when the finite interval $a \leq x \leq b$ is replaced by an infinite interval, for example $a \leq x < \infty$.

The following result, which we shall need in Chapter 7, represents a slight extension of Theorem 2f.

A function $f(x)$ is piecewise continuous on $a' \leq x \leq a''$ if there exist a finite number of points $a' = a_0 < a_1 < \cdots < a_m = a''$ and a corresponding set of functions $f_k(x)$ $(k = 1, \cdots, m)$ with $f_k(x)$ defined and continuous on $a_{k-1} \leq x \leq a_k$ such that $f(x) = f_k(x)$ for $a_{k-1} < x < a_k$.

THEOREM 3c. Let $f(x)$ be piecewise continuous on $a' \leq x \leq a''$. Let $g_N(x)$ $(N = 0, 1, \cdots)$ be continuous on $a' \leq x \leq a''$. If

1. there is a constant M such that $|f(x)| \leq M$, $|g_n(x)| \leq M$ for $a' \leq x \leq a''$, $N = 0, 1, \cdots$,

2. for each k and each[1] $\delta > 0$ $\lim\limits_{N \to \infty} g_N(x) = f(x)$ uniformly for $a_{k-1} + \delta < x < a_k - \delta$,

then it follows that

$$\lim_{N \to \infty} \int_{a'}^{a''} g_N(x)\, dx = \int_{a'}^{a''} f(x)\, dx.$$

Proof. Let $\epsilon > 0$ be given. Choose a $\delta > 0$ with the property that $m\delta + 4Mm\delta < \epsilon$. By Assumption 2 and Theorem 2b

$$\lim_{N \to \infty} \int_{a_{k-1}+\delta}^{a_k-\delta} [g_N(x) - f(x)]\, dx = 0 \qquad (k = 1, \cdots, m).$$

It follows that there is an index N_0 such that if $N \geq N_0$

(1) $$\left| \int_{a_{k-1}+\delta}^{a_k-\delta} [g_N(x) - f(x)]\, dx \right| < \delta \qquad (k = 1, \cdots, m).$$

By Assumption 1, $|g_N(x) - f(x)| \leq |g_n(x)| + |f(x)| \leq 2M$ on $a' \leq x \leq a''$; thus

(2) $$\left| \int_{a_0}^{a_0+\delta} [g_N(x) - f(x)]\, dx \right| \leq 2M\delta,$$

(3) $$\left| \int_{a_k-\delta}^{a_k+\delta} [g_N(x) - f(x)\, dx \right| \leq 4M\delta \qquad (k = 1, \cdots, m-1),$$

(4) $$\left| \int_{a_m-\delta}^{a_m} [g_N(x) - f(x)]\, dx \right| \leq 2M\delta.$$

Combining all these inequalities (1) through (4), we find that if $N \geq N_0$,

$$\left| \int_{a'}^{a''} [g_N(x) - f(x)]\, dx \right| < m\delta + 4Mm\delta \leq \epsilon.$$

PROBLEMS

1. Prove Theorem 3b.

[1] It is of course assumed that δ has been taken so small that $a_{k-1} + \delta < a_k - \delta$ for $k = 1, \ldots, m$.

4. Summation by Parts

The Weierstrass test (Theorem 2g) establishes uniform convergence by means of a uniform comparison test. Consequently it applies only to series which are absolutely convergent. The present section is devoted to a method by which certain series of functions which are not absolutely convergent may nevertheless be shown to be uniformly convergent. This method may be regarded as a generalization of the discussion of alternating series given in Sec. 8 of Chapter 1.

Given $\{a_k\}_{k=0}^{\infty}$, $\{\alpha_k\}_{k=0}^{\infty}$, we set

(1) $$s_m = \sum_{k=0}^{m} a_k, \qquad \delta_m = \alpha_m - \alpha_{m+1} \qquad (m = 0, 1, \cdots).$$

LEMMA 4a. With the above notations we have

$$\sum_{k=0}^{n} a_k \alpha_k = \sum_{k=0}^{n} s_k \delta_k + s_n \alpha_{n+1}.$$

Proof. This result is the analogue for finite sums of integration by parts for integrals. We have $a_k = s_k - s_{k-1}$ $(k = 0, 1, \cdots, n)$ where $s_{-1} = 0$. Thus

$$\sum_{k=0}^{n} a_k \alpha_k = (s_0 - s_{-1})\alpha_0 + (s_1 - s_0)\alpha_1 + \cdots + (s_{n-1} - s_{n-2})\alpha_{n-1} + (s_n - s_{n-1})\alpha_n$$

$$= -s_{-1}\alpha_0 + s_0(\alpha_0 - \alpha_1) + \cdots + s_{n-1}(\alpha_{n-1} - \alpha_n) + s_n(\alpha_n - \alpha_{n+1})$$

$$+ s_n \alpha_{n+1}$$

$$= \sum_{k=0}^{n} s_k \delta_k + s_n \alpha_{n+1} \qquad\qquad \text{since } s_{-1} = 0.$$

Before proving any theorems on uniform convergence, we shall illustrate our methods by proving some results on simple convergence.

THEOREM 4b. Let $\{a_k\}_{k=0}^{\infty}$, $\{\alpha_k\}_{k=0}^{\infty}$ be given, and let s_m and δ_m be defined by (1). If

1. there is a constant M such that $|s_m| \leq M$ $(m = 0, 1, \cdots)$,
2. $\alpha_0 \geq \alpha_1 \geq \alpha_2 \geq \cdots \geq 0$,
3. $\lim\limits_{k \to \infty} \alpha_k = 0$,

then the series $\sum\limits_{k=0}^{\infty} a_k \alpha_k$ converges.

Proof. We have $\sum\limits_{0}^{n} |\delta_k| = \sum\limits_{0}^{n} \delta_k = \alpha_0 - \alpha_{n+1} \leq \alpha_0$ $(n = 0, 1, \cdots)$.

It follows from this that $\sum_0^\infty \delta_k$ converges absolutely. The series $\sum_{k=0}^\infty s_k \delta_k$ also converges absolutely since $|s_k \delta_k| \leq M|\delta_k|$ by Assumption 1. Let $\sigma = \sum_{k=0}^\infty s_k \delta_k$; we shall prove that $\sum_{k=0}^\infty a_k \alpha_k = \sigma$. By Lemma 4a

$$\sum_{k=0}^n a_k \alpha_k = \sum_{k=0}^n s_k \delta_k + s_n \alpha_{n+1} .$$

Since $\lim\limits_{n\to\infty} \sum\limits_{k=0}^n s_k \delta_k = \sigma$ by definition and since by Assumptions 1 and 3, $\lim\limits_{n\to\infty} s_n \alpha_{n+1} = 0$, our desired result follows.

EXAMPLE 1. Theorem 8a of Chapter 1 (on alternating series) asserts that if $\alpha_0 \geq \alpha_1 \geq \alpha_2 \geq \alpha_3 \cdots \geq 0$ and if $\lim\limits_{n\to\infty} \alpha_n = 0$, the series $\sum\limits_{n=0}^\infty (-1)^n \alpha_n$ is convergent. This result is a corollary of Theorem 4b if we set $a_k = (-1)^k$ $(k = 0, 1, \cdots)$.

The following result is a slight variation on the same theme.

THEOREM 4c. Let $\{a_k\}_0^\infty$, $\{\alpha_k\}_0^\infty$ be given, and let s_m and δ_m be defined by **(1)**. If

1. $\sum_0^\infty a_k$ converges,

2. $\alpha_0 \geq \alpha_1 \geq \alpha_2 \geq \cdots \geq 0$,

then the series $\sum_0^\infty a_k \alpha_k$ converges.

Proof. By Lemma 4a

$$\sum_{k=0}^n a_k \alpha_k = \sum_{k=0}^n s_k \delta_k + s_n \alpha_{n+1} .$$

Since

(2)
$$\sum_{k=0}^n \delta_k = \alpha_0 - \alpha_{n+1} ,$$

we find that for any s

(3)
$$\sum_{k=0}^n a_k \alpha_k = \sum_{k=0}^n (s_k - s) \delta_k + (s_n - s) \alpha_{n+1} + s\alpha_0 .$$

Let us take $s = \sum\limits_0^\infty a_n$ so that $\lim\limits_{n\to\infty} (s_n - s) = 0$. There evidently exists a constant M such that $|s_n - s| \leq M$ $(n = 0, 1, \cdots)$. It follows (see the proof of Theorem

4b) that the series $\sum_0^\infty (s_k - s) \delta_k$ converges absolutely. Now $|(s_n - s) \alpha_{n+1}|$ $\leq |s_n - s| \alpha_0$, and thus $\lim_{n \to \infty} (s_n - s) \alpha_{n+1} = 0$. It follows that

$$\sum_0^\infty a_k \alpha_k = \sum_0^\infty (s_k - s) \delta_k + s\alpha_0 .$$

We now apply our methods to obtain a result on uniform convergence.

THEOREM 4d. Let $\{a_n\}_0^\infty$ and $\{\alpha_n(x)\}_0^\infty$ $(x \in S)$ be given. If

1. $\Sigma_0^\infty a_n$ converges,
2. $M \geq \alpha_0(x) \geq \alpha_1(x) \geq \cdots \geq 0$ $(x \in S)$ (here M is any finite constant),

then the series

$$\sum_{k=0}^\infty a_k \alpha_k(x)$$

converges uniformly for $x \in S$.

Proof. For each fixed x the argument used in the proof of Theorem 4c shows that

$$\sum_0^\infty a_k \alpha_k(x) = \sigma(x)$$

where $\qquad \sigma(x) = \sum_0^\infty (s_k - s) \delta_k(x) + s\alpha_0(x)$

To show that the convergence is uniform, we note that by Formula (**3**)

$$\sigma(x) - \sum_{k=0}^n a_k \alpha_k(x) = \sum_{n+1}^\infty (s_k - s) \delta_k(x) - (s_n - s) \alpha_{n+1}(x) .$$

Given $\epsilon > 0$, let us choose N so large than $n \geq N$ implies that $|s_n - s| < \epsilon/2M$, where M is the constant in Assumption 2. Since $0 \leq \alpha_{n+1}(x) \leq \alpha_0(x) \leq M$, it follows that

$$|(s_n - s) \alpha_{n+1}(x)| < \frac{\epsilon}{2M} \cdot M = \frac{\epsilon}{2} \qquad \text{for } n \geq N, x \in S .$$

Again formula (**2**) implies that $\Sigma_0^\infty |\delta_k(x)| \leq M$. Thus

$$\left| \sum_{n+1}^\infty (s_k - s) \delta_k(x) \right| < \frac{\epsilon}{2M} \sum_{n+1}^\infty |\delta_k(x)| \leq \frac{\epsilon}{2M} \cdot M = \frac{\epsilon}{2} \qquad \text{for } n \geq N, x \in S .$$

Thus we have proved that

$$\left| \sigma(x) - \sum_0^n a_k \, \alpha_k(x) \right| < \frac{\epsilon}{2} + \frac{\epsilon}{2} = \epsilon \qquad \text{for } n \geq N, \, x \in S.$$

EXAMPLE 2. Consider the function

(4)
$$L(x) = \sum_{n=1}^{\infty} (-1)^n \, n^{-x} \, .$$

Using the methods of Chapter 1 we easily see that the series (4) converges conditionally for $0 < x \leq 1$ and converges absolutely for $1 < x < \infty$. By means of the Weierstrass test, it may be shown as in Example 3 of Sec. 3 that the series (4) converges uniformly for $a \leq x < \infty$ for any number $a > 1$. Using Theorem 4d, we shall prove that in fact the series (4) converges uniformly for $a \leq x < \infty$ for any number $a > 0$. Let $a_n = (-1)^n \, n^{-a}$. Then by Theorem 8a of Chapter 1, $\sum_1^{\infty} a_n$ converges. Further let $\alpha_n(x) = n^{a-x}$ $(n = 1, 2, \cdots)$. The assumptions of Theorem 4d are satisfied and our assertion follows.

EXAMPLE 3. Discuss the convergence and the uniform convergence of the series

(5)
$$\sum_{k=0}^{\infty} (-1)^k \frac{x^k}{k} \, .$$

The methods of Chapter 1 suffice to show that the series above converges absolutely for $-1 < x < 1$, the series converges conditionally for $x = 1$, and diverges for $-\infty < x \leq -1$ and for $1 < x < \infty$. Choose a $(0 < a < 1)$. Then

$$\left| (-1)^k \frac{x^k}{k} \right| \leq \frac{a^k}{k} \qquad (|x| \leq a, \quad k = 0, 1, \cdots) \, .$$

Thus by Theorem 2h the series (5) converges uniformly for $|x| \leq a < 1$. Next let $a_k = (-1)^k/k$, $\alpha_k(x) = x^k$ $(k = 0, 1, \cdots)$. Then $\sum_1^{\infty} a_k$ converges, and if $0 \leq x \leq 1$, then $1 = \alpha_0(x) \geq \alpha_1(x) \geq \cdots \geq 0$. By Theorem 4d the series (5) converges uniformly for $0 \leq x \leq 1$. Combining these results, we see that (5) converges uniformly for $-a \leq x \leq 1$ for any $a(0 < a < 1)$. See in this connection Problem 4 of Sec. 1.

We state the following result without proof, the demonstration being left as an exercise for the reader.

THEOREM 4e. Let α_n, $a_n(x)$ $(x \in S)$ be defined for $n = 0, 1, 2, \cdots$. If

1. $\left| \sum_{k=0}^n a_k(x) \right| \leq M \qquad (x \in S, \quad n = 0, 1, \cdots),$

2. $\alpha_0 \geq \alpha_1 \geq \alpha_2 \geq \cdots \geq 0,$

3. $\lim\limits_{k\to\infty} \alpha_k = 0$,

then

$$\sum_0^\infty a_n(x)\,\alpha_n$$

converges uniformly for $x \in S$.

PROBLEMS

1. Discuss the convergence and uniform convergence of the series

$$\sum_{k=2}^\infty (-1)^k\,(\log k)^{-x}\,.$$

2. Discuss the convergence and uniform convergence of the series

$$\sum_{k=1}^\infty \cos\!\left(\frac{\pi k}{3}\right) k^{-x}\,.$$

3. Discuss the convergence and uniform convergence of the series

$$\sum_{k=0}^\infty \frac{(2x)^k}{(k+1)}\,.$$

4. Discuss the convergence and uniform convergence of the series

$$\sum_{k=1}^\infty (-1)^k\,\frac{x^{2k}}{\sqrt{k}}\,.$$

5. Discuss the convergence and uniform convergence of the series

$$\sum_{k=1}^\infty \cos \alpha k\; k^{-x}\,.$$

Here α is a fixed parameter $0 < \alpha < \pi$. HINT: Use Lemma 4a of Chapter 3.

6. Use Theorem 4e and Lemma 4a of Chapter 3 to show that if $a_1 \ge a_2 \ge \cdots \ge 0$, $\lim\limits_{k\to\infty} a_k = 0$, then the series

$$\sum_{k=1}^\infty a_k \cos kx$$

converges uniformly for $0 < \epsilon \le |x| \le \pi$.

7. Prove Theorem 4e.

8. A sequence $\{\alpha_k\}_0^\infty$ is said to be of "bounded variation" if $\sum_0^\infty |\delta_k|$ converges

where $\delta_k = \alpha_k - \alpha_{k+1}$. Prove that if there exist sequences $\{\beta_k\}_0^\infty$ and $\{\gamma_k\}_0^\infty$ with the properties:

(a) $\beta_0 \geq \beta_1 \geq \beta_2 \geq \cdots \geq 0, \gamma_0 \geq \gamma_1 \geq \gamma_2 \geq \cdots \geq 0,$

(b) $a_k = \beta_k - \gamma_k,$

then $\{\alpha_k\}_0^\infty$ is of bounded variation. Is the representation $\alpha_k = \beta_k - \gamma_k$ unique? Explain.

9. Prove that if $\{\alpha_k\}_0^\infty$ is of bounded variation, there exist sequences $\{\beta_k\}_0^\infty$ and $\{\gamma_k\}_0^\infty$ with the Properties a and b in Problem 8.

HINT: Let $\delta_k^+ = \alpha_k - \alpha_{k+1}$ if $\alpha_k - \alpha_{k+1} > 0$; otherwise let $\delta_k^+ = 0$. Similarly let $\delta_k^- = -(\alpha_k - \alpha_{k+1})$ if $-(\alpha_k - \alpha_{k+1}) > 0$; otherwise let $\delta_k^- = 0$. Show that if b and c are correctly chosen, one may take $\beta_k = b + \Sigma_k^\infty \delta_j^+$ and $\gamma_k = c + \Sigma_k^\infty \delta_j^-$.

10. Use the result of Problem 9 to show that Theorem 4c is true if the assumption "$\alpha_0 \geq \alpha_1 \geq \alpha_2 \geq \cdots \geq 0$" is replaced by the assumption "$\{\alpha_k\}_0^\infty$ is of bounded variation."

11. Show that in Problem 9 if it is assumed in addition that $\lim_{k\to\infty} \alpha_k = 0$, then $\{\beta_k\}_0^\infty$ and $\{\gamma_k\}_0^\infty$ can be so chosen that in addition to satisfying Properties a and b of Problem 8 $\{\beta_k\}_1^\infty$ and $\{\gamma_k\}_1^\infty$ also satisfy $\lim_{k\to\infty} \beta_k = 0, \lim_{k\to\infty} \gamma_k = 0$. Using this, generalize Theorem 4b.

[5]

Rearrangements, Double Series, Summability

1. Generalized Partial Sums

Let \mathfrak{P} be the set of all nonnegative integers $\mathfrak{P} = \{0, 1, 2, \cdots\}$. We denote by \mathcal{U} the following simple family of subsets of \mathfrak{P}:

$$U_0 = \{0\},$$

$$U_1 = \{0, 1\},$$
$$\vdots$$
$$U_n = \{0, 1, \cdots, n\},$$
$$\vdots$$

If $\sum_{k=0}^{\infty} a_k$ is any infinite series, the relation

$$(1) \qquad \qquad \sum_{k=0}^{\infty} a_k = a$$

may be written alternatively in the form

$$(2) \qquad \qquad \lim_{k \to \infty} \sum_{k \in U_n} a_k = a.$$

This is true because $\sum_{k \in U_n} a_k$ is the sum of those a_k's for which $k \in U_n = \{0, 1, \cdots, n\}$; that is, $\sum_{k \in U_n} a_k = \sum_{k=0}^{n} a_k$.

This suggests the following generalization. Let \mathcal{S} be any family of subsets of \mathfrak{P}, S_0, S_1, \cdots, satisfying the following conditions:

1. S_i is finite $(i = 0, 1, \cdots)$;
(3) 2. $S_i \subset S_{i+1}$ $(i = 0, 1, \cdots)$;
 3. for every $n \in \mathfrak{P}$ there is an index i such that $n \in S_i$.

For $i \in \mathfrak{P}$ we set

$$(4) \qquad \qquad \sigma_i = \sum_{n \in S_i} a_n;$$

σ_i is then the generalized partial sum of index i corresponding to \mathcal{S}.

DEFINITION 1a. If \mathscr{S} is a system satisfying the conditions of (**3**) and if $\sum_{k=0}^{\infty} a_k$ is an infinite series, we write $(\mathscr{S}) \sum_{k=0}^{\infty} a_k = a$

if
$$\lim_{i \to \infty} \sigma_i = a$$

where σ_i is defined by (**4**).

The value $(\mathscr{S}) \sum_{k=0}^{\infty} a_k$ (when it exists) is thus the limit of a sequence of generalized partial sums σ_i where in the ith generalized partial sum, $\sigma_i = \sum_{n \in S_i} a_n$, we have added all the terms a_n for which $n \in S_i$.

The following results state that in several important respects $(\mathscr{S}) \sum_0^{\infty}$ behaves quite like \sum_0^{∞}.

THEOREM 1b. Let \mathscr{S} satisfy the conditions of (**3**). Then

 1. if $(\mathscr{S}) \sum_0^{\infty} a_k = a$, then $(\mathscr{S}) \sum_0^{\infty} ca_k = ca$;

 2. if $(\mathscr{S}) \sum_0^{\infty} a_k = a$ and $(\mathscr{S}) \sum_0^{\infty} b_k = b$, then $(\mathscr{S}) \sum_0^{\infty} a_k + b_k = a + b$.

THEOREM 1c. Let \mathscr{S} satisfy the conditions of (**3**), and let $0 \leq a_k \leq b_k$ $(k = 0, 1, \cdots)$. Then if $(\mathscr{S}) \sum_0^{\infty} b_k$ exists, so does $(\mathscr{S}) \sum_0^{\infty} a_k$.

The demonstrations of these results are left to the reader as exercises.

We are now in the position of having for a given infinite series not merely one sum but an infinite number of sums one for each system satisfying Conditions 1–3 of (**3**). The object of the present section is to discuss the relations between these different "sums." We begin with an example.

EXAMPLE 1. Let \mathscr{E} be the family E_0, E_1, \cdots, where $E_n = \{0, 1, 2, \cdots, 2n\}$, and let \mathscr{O} be the family $0_0, 0_1, 0_2, \cdots$, where $0_n = \{0, 1, 2, \cdots, 2n + 1\}$. Then if $a_k = (-1)^k$ $(k = 0, 1, \cdots)$, we find that

$$(\mathscr{E}) \sum_0^{\infty} a_k = 1 ,$$

$$(\mathscr{O}) \sum_0^{\infty} a_k = 0 ,$$

$$(\mathscr{U}) \sum_0^{\infty} a_k \quad \text{does not exist.}$$

The principal result of the present section is that the behavior of Example 1 cannot occur if the a_k's are all of the same sign.

THEOREM 1d. Let $\mathscr{S} = \{S_i\}_0^{\infty}$ and $\mathscr{T} = \{T_i\}_0^{\infty}$ satisfy (**3**). If $a_k \geq 0$ $(k = 0, 1, 2, \cdots)$ and if $(\mathscr{S}) \sum_0^{\infty} a_k$ exists, then $(\mathscr{T}) \sum_0^{\infty} a_k$ exists and they are equal.

Proof. Since the a_k's are nonnegative, it follows from Condition 2 that

$$\sum_{k \in S_n} a_k \le \sum_{k \in S_{n+1}} a_k \qquad (n = 0, 1, \cdots);$$

that is, the sequence of "\mathscr{S}" partial sums is nondecreasing. Similarly

$$\sum_{k \in T_m} a_k \le \sum_{k \in T_{m+1}} a_k \qquad (m = 0, 1, \cdots).$$

Consider a set T_m in \mathscr{T}. It follows from Conditions 2 and 3, that if n is sufficiently large (depending upon m), then $T_m \subset S_n$. Using once again the fact that the a_k's are nonnegative, we find that

$$\sum_{k \in T_m} a_k \le \sum_{k \in S_n} a_k \le (\mathscr{S}) \sum_0^\infty a_k .$$

Since this is true for every m, we have

$$(\mathscr{T}) \sum_{k=0}^\infty a_k \le (\mathscr{S}) \sum_{k=0}^\infty a_k .$$

Reversing the roles of \mathscr{S} and \mathscr{T}, the same argument gives

$$(\mathscr{S}) \sum_{k=0}^\infty a_k \le (\mathscr{T}) \sum_{k=0}^\infty a_k ,$$

and our theorem follows.

We can easily extend this result to series $\sum_0^\infty a_k$, the terms of which are of mixed sign. It is natural to say that a series is \mathscr{S}-absolutely convergent if $(\mathscr{S}) \sum_0^\infty |a_k|$ exists. But by Theorem 1d if $(\mathscr{S}) \sum_0^\infty |a_k|$ exists, so does $(\mathscr{T}) \sum_0^\infty |a_k|$, that is, if a series is \mathscr{S}-absolutely convergent, it is \mathscr{T}-absolutely convergent. Consequently we may drop the prefix and simply use absolutely convergent to mean absolutely convergent with respect to any system \mathscr{S} satisfying Conditions 1–3. This is entirely consistent with Sec. 7 of Chapter 1.

THEOREM 1e. *Let \mathscr{S} and \mathscr{T} satisfy the conditions of (3). If $\sum_0^\infty a_k$ is absolutely convergent, then*

$$(\mathscr{S}) \sum_0^\infty a_k = (\mathscr{T}) \sum_0^\infty a_k .$$

Proof. Let $a_k^+ = \max\{a_k, 0\}$, $a_k^- = \{\max - a_k, 0\}$. Then

$$a_k^+ \ge 0, \ a_k^- \ge 0, \qquad a_k = a_k^+ - a_k^-, \qquad |a_k| = a_k^+ + a_k^- .$$

The last relation implies that $0 \le a_k^+ \le |a_k|$, $0 \le a_k^- \le |a_k|$. By Theorem 1c,

$(\mathscr{S}) \sum_0^\infty a_k^+, (\mathscr{S}) \sum_0^\infty a_k^-, (\mathscr{T}) \sum_0^\infty a_k^+$, and $(\mathscr{T}) \sum_0^\infty a_k^-$ all converge. By Theorem 1d

$$(\mathscr{S}) \sum_0^\infty a_k^+ = (\mathscr{T}) \sum_0^\infty a_k^+, \qquad (\mathscr{S}) \sum_0^\infty a_k^- = (\mathscr{T}) \sum_0^\infty a_k^- .$$

By Theorem 1c, however,

$$(\mathscr{S}) \sum_0^\infty a_k = (\mathscr{S}) \sum_0^\infty a_k^+ - (\mathscr{S}) \sum_0^\infty a_k^-,$$

$$(\mathscr{T}) \sum_0^\infty a_k = (\mathscr{T}) \sum_0^\infty a_k^+ - (\mathscr{T}) \sum_0^\infty a_k^-,$$

and our desired result follows.

The converse of Theorem 1e is true.

THEOREM 1f. If $\{a_k\}_0^\infty$ has the property that $(\mathscr{S}) \sum_0^\infty a_k$ exists for every system \mathscr{S} satisfying (3), then $\sum_0^\infty a_k$ is absolutely convergent.

Proof. If $\sum_0^\infty a_k$ is not absolutely convergent, one (or both) of the series $\sum_0^\infty a_k^+$ and $\sum_0^\infty a_k^-$ diverge. Suppose that $\sum_0^\infty a_k^+$ diverges ($\sum_0^\infty a_k^-$ may diverge or may not). Since the terms a_k^+ are nonnegative, the nondecreasing sequence $\sum_{k=0}^n a_k^+$ must be unbounded. For each m, take the smallest integer $n(m)$ such that

$$\sum_{k=0}^{n(m)} a_k^+ \geq \sum_0^m a_k^- + m.$$

Now define $S_m = S_m' \cup S_m''$ where

$$S_m' = \{k \mid 0 \leq k \leq n(m) \text{ and } a_k^+ > 0\},$$
$$S_m'' = \{k \mid 0 \leq k \leq m \quad \text{and } a_k \leq 0\}.$$

Then since $S_m' \cap S_m'' = \varnothing$,

$$\sum_{k \in S_m} a_k = \sum_{k \in S_m'} a_k + \sum_{k \in S_m''} a_k .$$

Now $$\sum_{k \in S_m'} a_k = \sum_0^{n(m)} a_k^+ \quad \text{and} \quad \sum_{k \in S_m''} a_k = - \sum_0^m a_k^-$$

so that

$$\sum_{k \in S_m} a_k \geq m \qquad (m = 1, 2, \cdots).$$

It follows that $(\mathscr{S}) \sum_0^\infty a_k = \lim_{m \to \infty} \sum_{k \in S_m} a_k$ does not exist.

COROLLARY 1g. If $\{a_k\}_0^\infty$ has the property that $(\mathscr{S}) \sum_0^\infty a_k$ exists for every system \mathscr{S} satisfying Conditions 1–3 of (3), the value $(\mathscr{S}) \sum_0^\infty a_k$ is the same for all \mathscr{S}.

A sequence of integers N_0, N_1, N_2, \cdots, is said to be a "rearrangement" of $\mathfrak{P} = \{0, 1, 2, \cdots\}$ if every element of \mathfrak{P} appears once and only once in $\{N_0, N_1, N_2, \cdots\}$. If $\{N_0, N_1, N_2, \cdots\}$ is a rearrangement of \mathfrak{P} and if we define \mathscr{S} by

$$S_0 = \{N_0\},$$
$$S_1 = \{N_0, N_1\},$$
$$\vdots$$
$$S_n = \{N_0, N_1, N_2, \cdots N_n\},$$

then \mathscr{S} satisfies conditions (3). The nth generalized partial sum (using \mathscr{S}) of the series $\sum_0^\infty a_k$ is then $\sum_{k \in S_n} a_k = a_{N_0} + a_{N_1} + \cdots + a_{N_n}$, and this is the same as the nth ordinary partial sum (using \mathscr{U}) of the "rearranged series" $\sum_0^\infty a_{N_k}$. Thus instead of using generalized partial sums one could more or less equivalently consider rearrangements of series.

PROBLEMS

1. Prove Theorem 1b.

2. Prove Theorem 1c.

3. Theorem 3d of Chapter 1 asserts that if $(\mathscr{U}) \sum_0^\infty t_n$ exists, so does $\lim_{n \to \infty} t_n = 0$.

Is this true if \mathscr{U} is replaced by an arbitrary \mathscr{S} satisfying (3)? Justify your answer.

4. Let \mathscr{S} and \mathscr{T} satisfy (3). We write $\mathscr{S} \wr \mathscr{T}$ if every S_i is some T_j. For example $\mathscr{E} \wr \mathscr{U}$. Prove that if $\mathscr{S} \wr \mathscr{T}$ and if $(\mathscr{T}) \sum_{n=0}^\infty a_n$ exists, then $(\mathscr{S}) \sum_{n=0}^\infty a_n$ exists and they are equal.

5. Is the assumption $\mathscr{S} \wr \mathscr{T}$ necessary for the conclusion of Problem 4? Justify your answer.

6. Show that if $\phi(i)$ is a function from \mathfrak{P} to \mathfrak{P} satisfying $\phi(i) > \phi(j)$ if $i > j$ and if $\mathscr{S} = \{S_0, S_1, S_2, \cdots\}$ satisfies (3), then so does $\mathscr{S}^1 = \{S_{\phi(0)}, S_{\phi(1)}, S_{\phi(2)}, \cdots\}$, and $\mathscr{S}^1 \wr \mathscr{S}$.

2. Double Series

Consider a doubly indexed set of numbers $a_{m,n}$ ($m,n = 0, 1, 2, \cdots$). By this we mean that on the set $\mathfrak{P} \times \mathfrak{P}$ of all ordered pairs of nonnegative integers there is defined a real valued function whose value at (n,m) is $a_{n,m}$. We thus have a number $a_{n,m}$ for each point (n,m) with $n \geq 0$, $m \geq 0$ (Fig. 14).

We wish to add this infinite set of numbers; that is, we wish to attach a meaning to $\sum_{n,m=0}^{\infty} a_{n,m}$. In the corresponding one-dimensional problem where we had to define $\sum_{0}^{\infty} a_n$, we had one number a_n for each point of \mathfrak{P}, that is, for each point of the real line with a nonnegative integral coordinate (Fig. 15).

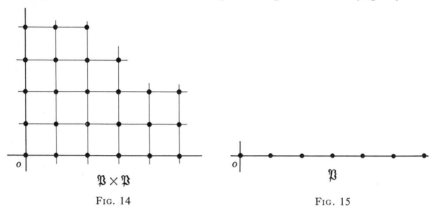

$$\mathfrak{P} \times \mathfrak{P}$$

FIG. 14

$$\mathfrak{P}$$

FIG. 15

In this case of all the family \mathscr{S} of sets satisfying the conditions of (**3**) of Sec. 1, the family \mathscr{U} was so much the simplest that we took as the definition of $\sum_{0}^{\infty} a_k$ the expression $\lim_{n \to \infty} \sum_{k \in U_n} a_k$. We now consider families of subsets \mathscr{S} of $\mathfrak{P} \times \mathfrak{P}$, S_0, S_1, S_2, \cdots, satisfying the conditions:

(**1**)
1. S_i is finite $(i = 0, 1, 2, \cdots)$;
2. $S_i \subset S_{i+1}$ $(i = 0, 1, 2, \cdots)$;
3. for every point (n,m) of $\mathfrak{P} \times \mathfrak{P}$ there is an index i such that $(n,m) \in S_i$.

Here we find that no one family of sets satisfying (**1**) is so much simpler than its competitors that it deserves to be taken as *the basis* of a definition of a two-dimensional sum.

EXAMPLE 1. (a) Let \mathscr{T} be the family T_0, T_0, T_2, \cdots, where $T_i = \{(n,m) \mid n + m \leq i\}$ (Fig. 16).

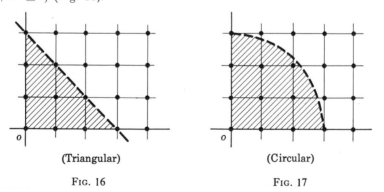

(Triangular)

FIG. 16

(Circular)

FIG. 17

(b) Let \mathscr{C} be the family C_0, C_1, C_2, \cdots, where $C_i = \{(n,m) \mid \sqrt{n^2 + m^2} \leq i\}$. (Fig. 17.)

(c) Let \mathscr{R} be the family R_0, R_1, R_2, \cdots, where $R_i = \{(n,m) \mid \max (n, m) \leq i\}$. (Fig. 18.)

(Square)

Fig. 18

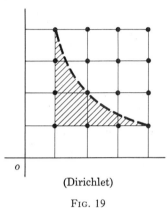

(Dirichlet)

Fig. 19

(d) Our last example is somewhat more erudite. Let $\mathfrak{P}_1 = \{1, 2, 3, \cdots\}$. Here we shall work with $\mathfrak{P}_1 \times \mathfrak{P}_1$ in place of $\mathfrak{P} \times \mathfrak{P}$. Let \mathscr{D} be the family D_1, D_2, D_3, \cdots, where $D_i = \{(n,m) \mid n \cdot m \leq i\}$. (Fig. 19.)

It is clear that no one of the families \mathscr{T}, \mathscr{C}, \mathscr{R}, or \mathscr{D} is really much simpler than the others. Thus in dealing with double series, we are from the very beginning forced to consider "generalized partial sums."

DEFINITION 2a. If \mathscr{S} is a family satisfying (1) and if $\sum_{n,m=0}^{\infty} a_{n,m}$ is a double infinite series, we write

$$(\mathscr{S}) \sum_{n,m=0}^{\infty} a_{n,m} = a$$

$$\lim_{i \to \infty} \sum_{(n,m) \in S_i} a_{n,m} = a .$$

The arguments given in Sec. 1 reapplied almost without change now give us the following.

THEOREM 2b. Let \mathscr{S} and \mathscr{T} satisfy (1). If $a_{n,m} \geq 0$ for $(n,m) \in \mathfrak{P} \times \mathfrak{P}$ and if $(\mathscr{S}) \sum_{n,m=0}^{\infty} a_{n,m}$ exists, then $(\mathscr{T}) \sum_{n,m=0}^{\infty} a_{n,m}$ exists and they are equal.

In consequence the definition of two-dimensional absolute convergence is independent of the family \mathscr{S}, and we have

THEOREM 2c. Let \mathscr{S} and \mathscr{T} satisfy (1). If $\sum_{n,m=0}^{\infty} a_{n,m}$ is absolutely convergent, then

$$(\mathscr{S}) \sum_{n,m=0}^{\infty} a_{n,m} = (\mathscr{T}) \sum_{n,m=0}^{\infty} a_{n,m}.$$

PROBLEMS

1. Let $\mathscr{S}^{(1)} = \{S_i^{(1)}\}_{i=0}^{\infty}$ and $\mathscr{S}^{(2)} = \{S_i^{(2)}\}_{i=0}^{\infty}$ be families of subsets of \mathfrak{P}, each satisfying the conditions of **(3)** of Sec. 1. Let $\mathscr{S} = \{S_i\}_0^{\infty}$ be the family of subsets of $\mathfrak{P} \times \mathfrak{P}$ defined by $S_i = S_i^{(1)} \times S_i^{(2)}$; that is, $S_i = \{(m,n) \mid m \in S_i^{(1)}$ and $n \in S_i^{(2)}\}$. Show that under these assumptions \mathscr{S} satisfies the conditions of **(1)** of Sec. 2.

2. Construct $a_{m,n}$, $(m,n) \in \mathfrak{P} \times \mathfrak{P}$, such that $(\mathscr{T})\ \Sigma_{m,n=0}^{\infty}\, a_{m,n}$ exists but $(\mathscr{R})\ \Sigma_{m,n=0}^{\infty}\, a_{m,n}$ does not. Similarly construct $b_{m,n}$, $(m,n) \in \mathfrak{P} \times \mathfrak{P}$, such that $(\mathscr{R})\ \Sigma_{m,n=0}^{\infty}\, b_{m,n}$ exists but $(\mathscr{T})\ \Sigma_{m,n=0}^{\infty}\, b_{m,n}$ does not.

3. Let $f(x,y)$ be continuous and nonnegative for $0 \le x,y < \infty$, and let $f(x,y)$ be decreasing in each variable separately; that is,

$$f(x,y_1) \ge f(x,y_2) \quad \text{if } y_2 \ge y_1, \qquad \text{and} \qquad f(x_1, y) \ge f(x_2, y) \quad \text{if } x_2 \ge x_1 .$$

Prove that

$$\sum_{m,n=1}^{i} f(m,n) \le \int_1^i \int_1^i f(x,y)\, dx\, dy + \int_1^i f(1,y)\, dy + \int_1^i f(x,1)\, dx + f(1,1).$$

Deduce that if there is a constant A such that for all $T \ge 1$

$$\int_1^T \int_1^T f(x,y)\, dx\, dy \le A, \quad \int_1^T f(x,1)\, dx \le A, \quad \int_1^T f(1,y)\, dy \le A,$$

then the series $\Sigma_{m,n=1}^{\infty}\, f(m,n)$ converges absolutely.

4. Under the same assumptions prove that

$$\sum_{m,n=1}^{i} f(m,n) \ge \int_1^{i+1} \int_1^{i+1} f(x,y)\, dx\, dy$$

$$\ge \int_1^{i+1} f(x,1)\, dx$$

$$\ge \int_1^{i+1} f(1,y)\, dy .$$

Deduce that if any one of the integrals

$$\int_1^T \int_1^T f(x,y)\, dx\, dy, \qquad \int_1^T f(x,1)\, dx, \qquad \int_1^T f(1,y)\, dy$$

is unbounded as $T \to \infty$, then $\Sigma_{m,n=1}^{\infty}\, f(m,n)$ diverges.

5. Use the results of Problems 3 and 4 to prove that

$$\sum_{m,n=1}^{\infty} n^{-\alpha}\, m^{-\beta}\, [\max\,(n,m)]^{-\gamma}$$

converges if $\alpha + \gamma > 1$, $\beta + \gamma > 1$, $\alpha + \beta + \gamma > 2$ and diverges otherwise.

6. State and prove comparison tests for convergence and divergence of series $\sum_{m,n=1}^{\infty} a_{m,n}$ with nonnegative terms.

7. Use the results of Problems 3–6 to test the following series for convergence or divergence:

(a) $\displaystyle\sum_{m,n=1}^{\infty} (m^2 + n^2)^{-\alpha};$

(b) $\displaystyle\sum_{m,n=1}^{\infty} (m^\beta + n^\beta)^{-1};$

(c) $\displaystyle\sum_{m,n=1}^{\infty} m^{-\alpha}(m^2 + n^2)^{-\beta};$

(d) $\displaystyle\sum_{m,n=1}^{\infty} mn\, 2^{-m-n}$

3. Products

In this section we shall apply the results of Sec. 2 to obtain some important results on the multiplication of power series and Dirichlet series. If we multiply two finite sums together, for example, $(a_0 + a_1 + a_2)(b_0 + b_1 + b_2)$, we obtain as the result the sum of all the products which can be formed by taking one term from the first factor and one term from the second. In our example we obtain the nine terms in Table 2. Each term is determined by two indices—the index of the term in the first factor and the index of the term in the second factor of which it is the product. This suggests the following result concerning infinite sums (series).

Table 2

b_2	$a_0 b_2$	$a_1 b_2$	$a_2 b_2$
b_1	$a_0 b_1$	$a_1 b_1$	$a_2 b_1$
b_0	$a_0 b_0$	$a_1 b_0$	$a_2 b_0$
	a_0	a_1	a_2

LEMMA 3a. If $\sum\limits_{0}^{\infty} a_m = a$, $\sum\limits_{0}^{\infty} b_n = b$, then

$$(\mathscr{R}) \sum_{m,n=0}^{\infty} a_m b_n = ab.$$

Proof. We have

$$(\mathscr{R}) \sum_{m,n=0}^{\infty} a_m b_n = \lim_{i \to \infty} \sum_{(m,n) \in R_i} a_m b_n.$$

Now $(m,n) \in R_i$ if max $(m,n) \leq i$. Thus a moments reflection shows that

$$\sum_{m,n \in R_i} a_m b_n = \left(\sum_{m=0}^{i} a_m\right) \left(\sum_{n=0}^{i} b_n\right).$$

By assumption $\lim\limits_{i \to \infty} \sum\limits_{m=0}^{i} a_m = a$, $\lim\limits_{i \to \infty} \sum\limits_{n=0}^{i} b_n = b$. We have only to apply Theorem 1d of Chapter 1 to complete our proof.

THEOREM 3b. If the series $\Sigma_{m=0}^{\infty} a_m = a$ and $\Sigma_{n=0}^{\infty} b_n = b$ are absolutely convergent and if \mathscr{S} is any method satisfying the conditions of (1) of Sec. 2, then

$$(\mathscr{S}) \sum_{m,n=0}^{\infty} a_m b_n = ab.$$

Proof. We shall first prove that $\Sigma_{m,n=0}^{\infty} a_m b_n$ is absolutely convergent. By assumption the series $\Sigma_{m=0}^{\infty} |a_m|$ and $\Sigma_{n=0}^{\infty} |b_n|$ are convergent; it follows from Lemma 3a that $(\mathscr{R}) \Sigma_{m,n=0}^{\infty} |a_m b_n|$ is convergent, and our assertion is proved. (See the remark which follows Theorem 2b.) Since $\Sigma_{m,n=0}^{\infty} a_m b_n$ is absolutely convergent, Theorem 2c implies that

$$(\mathscr{S}) \sum_{m,n=0}^{\infty} a_m b_n = (\mathscr{R}) \sum_{m,n=0}^{\infty} a_m b_n.$$

The following example shows that the conclusion of Theorem 3b may fail if absolute convergence is not assumed.

EXAMPLE 1. Let $a_m = b_m = \binom{-\frac{1}{2}}{m}$. We have

$$(-1)^m a_m = \frac{1}{2} \cdot \frac{3}{2} \cdots \frac{(2m-1)}{2} (m!)^{-1}.$$

Since $(-1)^{m+1} a_{m+1} = (-1)^m a_m (m + \frac{1}{2})/(m+1)$, it follows that the terms of the series are alternating in sign and decreasing in absolute value. Since

$(-1)^m a_m = \Gamma(m + \frac{1}{2}) [\Gamma(m + 1) \Gamma(\frac{1}{2})]^{-1}$, it is easy to see that $\lim\limits_{m \to \infty} (-1)^m a_m = 0$. See also problem 3 of Sec. 10 of Chapter 1. It follows from Sec. 8 of Chapter 1 that the (identical) series $\sum_{m=0}^{\infty} a_m$ and $\sum_{n=0}^{\infty} b_n$ converge. By Lemma 3a, $(\mathscr{R}) \sum_{m,n=0}^{\infty} a_m b_n$ exists. We shall show that $(\mathscr{T}) \sum_{m,n=0}^{\infty} a_m b_n$ does not. By definition $(\mathscr{T}) \sum_{m,n=0}^{\infty} a_m b_n = \lim\limits_{i \to \infty} \sigma_i$ where $\sigma_i = \sum_{(m,n) \in T_i} a_m b_n$. Now

$$\sigma_i = \sum_{n=0}^{i} \sum_{j=0}^{n} a_n b_{n-j},$$

$$\sum_{j=0}^{n} a_n b_{n-j} = \sum_{j=0}^{n} \binom{-\frac{1}{2}}{j} \binom{-\frac{1}{2}}{n-j} = \binom{-1}{n} = (-1)^n$$

by Problem 11 of Sec. 2 Chapter 2. Thus σ_i does not converge as $i \to \infty$, and our assertion is proved.

EXAMPLE 2. The series

$$E(x) = \sum_{k=0}^{\infty} \frac{x^k}{k!}$$

defines $E(x)$ as a function of x for $-\infty < x < \infty$. Prove [without identifying $E(x)$ as e^x] that

$$E(x + y) = E(x)E(y)$$

for all real x and y. By Lemma 3a

$$E(x)E(y) = (\mathscr{R}) \sum_{m,n=0}^{\infty} \frac{x^m}{m!} \frac{y^n}{n!}.$$

Let us compute

$$(\mathscr{T}) \sum_{m,n=0}^{\infty} \frac{x^m}{m!} \frac{y^n}{n!} = \lim_{i \to \infty} \sum_{m+n \leq i} \frac{x^m}{m!} \frac{y^n}{n!}$$

$$= \lim_{i \to \infty} \sum_{j=0}^{i} \sum_{m+n=j} \frac{x^m}{m!} \frac{y^n}{n!}.$$

Now

$$\sum_{m+n=j} \frac{x^m}{m!} \frac{y^n}{n!} = \frac{1}{j!} \sum_{n=0}^{j} x^{j-n} y^n \binom{j}{n}$$

$$= \frac{(x + y)^j}{j!}.$$

Thus

$$(\mathscr{T}) \sum_{m,n=0}^{\infty} \frac{x^m}{m!} \frac{y^n}{n!} = \lim_{i \to \infty} \sum_{j=0}^{i} \frac{(x + y)^j}{j!} = E(x + y).$$

Our demonstration would be complete if we knew that

$$(\mathscr{T}) \sum_{m,n=0}^{\infty} \frac{x^m}{m!} \frac{y^n}{n!} = (\mathscr{R}) \sum_{m,n=0}^{\infty} \frac{x^m}{m!} \cdot \frac{y^n}{n!}.$$

That this is true follows from Theorem 3b. As this example shows, the characteristic property of the exponential function can be read off from the exponential series.

Consider two power series with the same center c:

(1)
$$a_0 + a_1(x - c) + a_2(x - c)^2 + \cdots .$$
$$b_0 + b_1(x - c) + b_2(x - c)^2 + \cdots .$$

Table 3 lists all the products which can be formed using one term from the first series and one term from the second series.

Table 3

\vdots	\vdots	\vdots	\vdots	\vdots	\vdots
$b_3(x - c)^3$	$a_0 b_3(x - c)^3$	$a_1 b_3(x - c)^4$	$a_2 b_3(x - c)^5$	$a_3 b_3(x - c)^6$	\dots
$b_2(x - c)^2$	$a_0 b_2(x - c)^2$	$a_1 b_2(x - c)^3$	$a_2 b_2(x - c)^4$	$a_3 b_2(x - c)^5$	\dots
$b_1(x - c)$	$a_0 b_1(x - c)$	$a_1 b_1(x - c)^2$	$a_2 b_1(x - c)^3$	$a_3 b_1(x - c)^4$	\dots
b_0	$a_0 b_0$	$a_1 b_0(x - c)$	$a_2 b_0(x - c)^2$	$a_3 b_0(x - c)^3$	\dots
	a_0	$a_1(x - c)$	$a_2(x - c)^2$	$a_3(x - c)^3$	\dots

If we collect together those terms involving the same power of $(x - c)$, we obtain a (single) series

(2)
$$c_0 + c_1(x - c) + c_2(x - c)^2 + \cdots$$

where $c_0 = a_0 b_0$, $c_1 = a_1 b_0 + a_0 b_1$, $c_2 = a_2 b_0 + a_1 b_1 + a_0 b_2$, etc.

We now take as the definition of the *power series product* of the two series **(1)** the series **(2)**. Thus the power series product of two power series with center c is again a power series with center c. Now it is easily seen that

$$\sum_{k=0}^{i} c_k(x - c)^k = \sum_{(m,n) \in T_i} a_m(x - c)^m b_n(x - c)^n .$$

Applying Theorem 3b, we have the following result which is of great importance in the theory of power series.

THEOREM 3c. If for a given value of x the series

$$\sum_0^\infty a_m(x - c)^m, \qquad \sum_0^\infty b_n(x - c)^n,$$

converge absolutely, then the series

$$\sum_0^\infty c_k(x - c)^k \qquad \text{where} \qquad c_k = \sum_{m+n=k} a_m b_n$$

converges (absolutely) to the sum

$$\left[\sum_0^\infty a_m(x - c)^m\right]\left[\sum_0^\infty b_n(x - c)^n\right].$$

EXAMPLE 3. The series

$$c(x) = \sum_0^\infty \frac{(-1)^k}{(2k)!} x^{2k},$$

(3)

$$s(x) = \sum_0^\infty \frac{(-1)^k}{(2k+1)!} x^{2k+1}$$

define $c(x)$ and $s(x)$ as functions of x for $-\infty < x < \infty$. Prove from the series definitions of $c(x)$ and $s(x)$ [and without identifying $c(x)$ as cos x or $s(x)$ as sin x] that

$$2s(x)\, c(x) = s(2x).$$

Since the series **(3)** converge absolutely for all x, Theorem 3c implies

that

$$s(x)c(x) = \sum_0^\infty a_{2k+1}\, x^{2k+1}$$

where

$$a_{2k+1} = \sum_{j=0}^k \frac{(-1)^j}{(2j)!} \cdot \frac{(-1)^{k-j}}{(2k-2j+1)!}.$$

A simple transformation gives

$$a_{2k+1} = \frac{(-1)^k}{(2k+1)!} \sum_{j=0}^k \binom{2k+1}{2j}.$$

To evaluate the sum on the right, note that

$$2^{2k+1} = (1+1)^{2k+1} = \sum_{i=0}^{2k+1} \binom{2k+1}{i}.$$

$$0 = (1-1)^{2k+1} = \sum_{i=0}^{2k+1} \binom{2k+1}{i}(-1)^i.$$

Adding, we find that

$$2^{2k+1} = 2 \sum_0^k \binom{2k+1}{2j}.$$

$$a_{2k+1} = \frac{1}{2} \frac{(-1)^k \, 2^{2k+1}}{(2k+1)!};$$

thus

$$2s(x)c(x) = \sum_0^\infty \frac{(-1)^k \, (2x)^{2k+1}}{(2k+1)!} = s(2x).$$

Very similar considerations apply to the product of Dirichlet series. Consider the series

(4) $$\sum_1^\infty c_m m^{-s} \quad \text{and} \quad \sum_1^\infty d_n n^{-s}.$$

Again in Table 4 we list all possible products which can be formed using one term from the first series and one term from the second series.

Table 4

\vdots		\vdots	\vdots	\vdots	\vdots	\vdots	\vdots	\vdots	\vdots
$d_5 5^{-s}$		$c_1 d_5 5^{-s}$	$c_2 d_5 10^{-s}$	$c_3 d_5 15^{-s}$					\cdots
$d_4 4^{-s}$		$c_1 d_4 4^{-s}$	$c_2 d_4 8^{-s}$	$c_3 d_4 12^{-s}$					\cdots
$d_3 3^{-s}$		$c_1 d_3 3^{-s}$	$c_2 d_3 6^{-s}$	$c_3 d_3 9^{-s}$					\cdots
$d_2 2^{-s}$		$c_1 d_2 2^{-s}$	$c_2 d_2 4^{-s}$	$c_3 d_2 6^{-s}$	$c_4 d_2 8^{-s}$				\cdots
d_1		$c_1 d_1$	$c_2 d_1 2^{-s}$	$c_3 d_1 3^{-s}$	$c_4 d_1 4^{-s}$	$c_5 d_1 5^{-s}$			\cdots
		c_1	$c_2 2^{-s}$	$c_3 3^{-s}$	$c_4 4^{-s}$	$c_5 5^{-s}$		\cdots	

If we collect together those terms involving k^{-s} for fixed k, we obtain a single series

(5) $$e_1 + e_2 2^{-s} + e_3 3^{-s} + e_4 4^{-s} + e_5 5^{-s} + \cdots$$

where $e_1 = c_1 d_1$, $e_2 = c_2 d_1 + c_1 d_2$, $e_3 = c_3 d_1 + c_1 d_3$, $e_4 = c_4 d_1 + c_2 d_2 + c_1 d_4$, $e_5 = c_5 d_1 + c_1 d_5$, etc. The series (5) is the *Dirichlet product* of the two Dirichlet series (4).

THEOREM 3d. If for a given value of s the series

$$\sum_1^\infty c_m m^{-s} \quad \text{and} \quad \sum_1^\infty d_n n^{-s}$$

converge absolutely, then the series

$$\sum_1^\infty e_k k^{-s} \qquad \text{where} \qquad e_k = \sum_{m \cdot n = k} c_m d_n$$

converges (absolutely) to the sum

$$\left[\sum_1^\infty c_m m^{-s}\right]\left[\sum_1^\infty d_n n^{-s}\right].$$

Proof. Evident.

EXAMPLE 4. For $n \in \mathfrak{P}_1$ let $d(n)$ be the number of positive integers k which divide n, 1 and n included. For example, 1, 2, 3, and 6 divide 6; thus $d(6) = 4$. Prove that if

(6) $$\zeta(s) = \sum_1^\infty n^{-s} \qquad (s > 1),$$

then $$\zeta(s)^2 = \sum_1^\infty d(n) n^{-s}.$$

It is evident that the series (6) is absolutely convergent for $s > 1$. By Theorem 3d if $s > 1$, then

$$\zeta(s)^2 = \sum_1^\infty z_n n^{-s}$$

where $$z_n = \sum_{k \cdot j = n} 1 \cdot 1 = d(n),$$

and our assertion is proved.

PROBLEMS

1. Let $\mathscr{S}^{(1)}$, $\mathscr{S}^{(2)}$, and \mathscr{S} be defined as in Problem 1 of Sec. 2. Prove that if $(\mathscr{S}^{(1)}) \sum_0^\infty a_m = a$ and if $(\mathscr{S}^{(2)}) \sum_0^\infty b_n = b$, then $(\mathscr{S}) \sum_0^\infty a_m b_n = ab$.

2. Prove that if $s(x)$ and $c(x)$ are defined as in Example 3, then for all real x and y

$$s(x + y) = s(x)c(y) + s(y)c(x).$$

3. Prove that for all real x

$$c(2x) = 1 - 2s(x)^2 = 2c(x)^2 - 1.$$

Note this problem is to be done using the methods of Example 3.

4. For $n \in \mathfrak{P}_1$ let $\sigma(n)$ be the sum of the positive integers k which divide n, 1 and n included. For example, since 1, 2, 3, and 6 divide 6, $\sigma(6) = 12$. Prove that

$$\zeta(s)\, \zeta(s - 1) = \sum_1^\infty \sigma(n)\, n^{-s} \qquad (s > 2).$$

For $n \in \mathfrak{P}_1$ let $\mu(n)$ (the Möbius function) be defined as follows: $\mu(1) = 0$, $\mu(n) = 0$ if n has a squared factor, and $\mu(n) = (-1)^r$ if $n = p_1 p_2 \cdots p_r$ where the primes p_1, \cdots, p_r are all distinct. We assert that

$$\sum_{d \mid n} \mu(d) = \begin{cases} 1 & (n = 1) \\ 0 & (n > 1); \end{cases}$$

Here the summation is, as the notation indicates, extended over all positive integers d which divide n, 1 and n included. To see this suppose that $n > 1$ and that $n = p_1^{r_1} p_2^{r_2} \cdots p_s^{r_s}$ is the factorization of n into powers of distinct primes, then

$$\sum_{d \mid n} \mu(d) = 1 + \sum_i \mu(p_i) + \sum_{i<j} \mu(p_i p_j) + \cdots .$$

Now $\sum_i \mu(p_i)$ consists of $\binom{s}{1}$ terms all equal to -1; $\sum_{i<j} \mu(p_i p_j)$ consists of $\binom{s}{2}$ terms all equal to $+1$; etc. Thus if $s \geq 1$

$$\sum_{d \mid n} \mu(d) = \sum_{k=0}^{s} \binom{s}{k} (-1)^k = (1-1)^s = 0 .$$

5. Show that the Dirichlet series

$$\sum_1^\infty \mu(n) n^{-s}$$

converges absolutely for $s > 1$. Using the above, prove that

$$\sum_1^\infty \mu(n) n^{-s} = \frac{1}{\zeta(s)} \quad (s > 1) .$$

6. Let p_1, p_2, p_3, \cdots, be the prime numbers 2, 3, 5, \cdots . Show that

$$\prod_{k=1}^{n} (1 - p_k^{-s}) = \sum_{k \in A_n} \mu(k) k^{-s}$$

where

$$A_n = \{k \mid 1 \leq k \leq p_1 p_2 \cdots p_n \text{ and } k \text{ a product of powers of } p_1, \cdots p_n\} .$$

Show that if $\mathscr{A} = \{A_1, A_2, \cdots\}$, then \mathscr{A} satisfies the conditions of **(3)** of Sec. 1 (with \mathfrak{P} replaced by \mathfrak{P}_1). Deduce that if $s > 1$, then

$$\prod_1^\infty (1 - p_k^{-s}) = \lim_{m \to \infty} \prod_{k=1}^{m} (1 - p_k^{-s}) = \frac{1}{\zeta(s)} .$$

7. Prove that $\zeta(s) = \prod_{k=1}^{\infty} \left(\frac{1}{1 - p_k^{-s}} \right) (s > 1)$ where $\zeta(s)$ is Riemann's zeta function

or simply the zeta function. $\zeta(s)$ plays a central role in the theory of the distribution of prime numbers.

4. Fubini's Theorem

Let $a_{m,n}$ be defined on $\mathfrak{P} \times \mathfrak{P}$. Still another method for assigning a value to $\sum_{m,n=0}^{\infty} a_{m,n}$ is by means of the *iterated* sums

$$(1) \qquad \sum_{m=0}^{\infty} \left(\sum_{n=0}^{\infty} a_{m,n} \right). \qquad \text{and} \qquad \sum_{n=0}^{\infty} \left(\sum_{m=0}^{\infty} a_{m,n} \right)$$

In the first of these iterated sums we have begun by summing those terms $a_{m,n}$ which be in the mth row. Then these "subtotals" are summed over all the rows. In the second of the iterated sums we begun by summing those terms $a_{m,n}$ which lie in the nth column. Then these "subtotals" are summed over all columns. It is possible to consider such iterated sums within a general framework such as that introduced in Sec. 2. However we shall not do this here; we shall in fact confine ourselves to the demonstration of the following important result and its immediate corollaries.

THEOREM 4a. If $a_{m,n} \geq 0$, $(m,n) \in \mathfrak{P} \times \mathfrak{P}$, and if \mathscr{S} is any family of sets satisfying the conditions of (1) of Sec. 2, the existence of any one of the sums

$$(2) \qquad (\mathscr{S}) \sum_{m,n=0}^{\infty} a_{m,n}, \qquad \sum_{n=0}^{\infty} \left(\sum_{m=0}^{\infty} a_{m,n} \right), \qquad \sum_{m=0}^{\infty} \left(\sum_{n=0}^{\infty} a_{m,n} \right),$$

implies the existence of the others and their equality.

Proof. The demonstration is a slight modification of that given for Theorems 1d and 2b. It is evident that since $a_{m,n} \geq 0$, each sum in (2) is finite or $+\infty$. Let $S_i \in \mathscr{S}$. Chose n_0 so large that $S_i \subset \{(m,n) \mid n \leq n_0\}$. Then

$$\sum_{(m,n) \in S_i} a_{m,n} \leq \sum_{n=0}^{n_0} \left(\sum_{m=0}^{\infty} a_{m,n} \right) \leq \sum_{n=0}^{\infty} \left(\sum_{m=0}^{\infty} a_{m,n} \right),$$

and thus letting $i \to \infty$, we find

$$(\mathscr{S}) \sum_{n,m=0}^{\infty} a_{m,n} \leq \sum_{n=0}^{\infty} \left(\sum_{m=0}^{\infty} a_{m,n} \right).$$

To prove the reverse inequality, suppose first that $\sum_{m=0}^{\infty} a_{m,n}$ is finite for each n. Let $\epsilon > 0$ be fixed. Given n_0, we shall show that if the index i is chosen sufficiently large (depending on n_0 and ϵ), then

$$(3) \qquad \sum_{n=0}^{n_0} \left(\sum_{m=0}^{\infty} a_{m,n} \right) \leq \sum_{(m,n) \in S_i} a_{m,n} + \epsilon \leq (\mathscr{S}) \sum_{m,n=0}^{\infty} a_{m,n} + \epsilon.$$

Letting $n_0 \to \infty$, we shall then have

$$\sum_{n=0}^{\infty} \left(\sum_{m=0}^{\infty} a_{m,n} \right) \leq (\mathscr{S}) \sum_{m,n=0}^{\infty} a_{m,n} + \epsilon$$

or since ϵ is arbitrary

$$\sum_{n=0}^{\infty} \left(\sum_{m=0}^{\infty} a_{m,n} \right) \leq (\mathscr{S}) \sum_{m,n=0}^{\infty} a_{m,n} .$$

To prove (3), we note that for each n $(0 \leq n \leq n_0)$ we have

$$\lim_{k \to \infty} \sum_{m=0}^{k} a_{m,n} = \sum_{m=0}^{\infty} a_{m,n} .$$

By Theorem 1c of Chapter 1 it follows that

$$\lim_{k \to \infty} \sum_{n=0}^{n_0} \sum_{m=0}^{k} a_{m,n} = \sum_{n=0}^{n_0} \left(\sum_{m=0}^{\infty} a_{m,n} \right) .$$

Thus given $\epsilon > 0$, there is an index m_0 such that

$$\sum_{n=0}^{n_0} \left(\sum_{m=0}^{m_0} a_{m,n} \right) \geq \sum_{n=0}^{n_0} \left(\sum_{m=0}^{\infty} a_{m,n} \right) - \epsilon .$$

Now choose i so large that $\{m,n \mid 0 \leq m \leq m_0, 0 \leq n \leq n_0\} \subset S_i$, etc. There remains the case that for some n $\sum_{m=0}^{\infty} a_{m,n}$ is infinite. In this case both the sums

$$\sum_{n=0}^{\infty} \left(\sum_{m=0}^{\infty} a_{m,n} \right) \quad \text{and} \quad (\mathscr{S}) \sum_{m,n=0}^{\infty} a_{m,n}$$

are infinite.

We have proved that $(\mathscr{S}) \sum_{m,n=0}^{\infty} a_{m,n}$ and $\sum_{n=0}^{\infty} (\sum_{m=0}^{\infty} a_{m,n})$ are both $+\infty$ or are both finite and equal. An identical argument proves that $(\mathscr{S}) \sum_{m,n=0}^{\infty} a_{m,n}$ and $\sum_{m=0}^{\infty} (\sum_{n=0}^{\infty} a_{m,n})$ are both $+\infty$ or both finite and equal. Q.E.D.

It follows from Theorem 4a that the Three series

$$(\mathscr{S}) \sum_{m,n=0}^{\infty} |a_{m,n}|, \quad \sum_{n=0}^{\infty} \left(\sum_{m=0}^{\infty} |a_{m,n}| \right), \quad \sum_{m=0}^{\infty} \left(\sum_{n=0}^{\infty} |a_{m,n}| \right)$$

are all finite or are all $+\infty$. Thus the concept of absolute convergence remains unambiguous when extended to iterated sums. The standard arguments we have used before now suffice to prove

THEOREM 4b. Let \mathscr{S} satisfy the conditions of (1) of Sec. 2. If $\sum_{m,n=0}^{\infty} |a_{m,n}|$ is absolutely convergent, then

$$(\mathscr{S}) \sum_{m,n=0}^{\infty} a_{m,n} = \sum_{n=0}^{\infty} \left(\sum_{m=0}^{\infty} a_{m,n} \right) = \sum_{m=0}^{\infty} \left(\sum_{n=0}^{\infty} a_{m,n} \right).$$

This result is often referred to as Fubini's theorem for double series.

EXAMPLE 1. Let $a_{m,n}$ be defined by Table 5

Table 5

\vdots								\vdots	$\vdots\cdots$
5	0	0	0	0	0	1	$--1$	0	\cdots
4	0	0	0	0	1	-1	0	0	
3	0	0	0	1	-1	0	0	0	
2	0	0	1	-1	0	0	0	0	
1	0	1	-1	0	0	0	0	0	
0	1	-1	0	0	0	0	0	0	\cdots
$n \diagdown m$	0	1	2	3	4	5	6	7	\cdots

It is evident that

$$\sum_{n=0}^{\infty} \left(\sum_{m=0}^{\infty} a_{m,n} \right) = 0, \qquad \sum_{m=0}^{\infty} \left(\sum_{n=0}^{\infty} a_{m,n} \right) = 1.$$

Needless to say the series $\sum_{m,n=0}^{\infty} a_{m,n}$ is *not* absolutely convergent.

EXAMPLE 2. Prove that

$$\sum_{n=0}^{\infty} \frac{1}{n!} \left(\frac{x}{2}\right)^n J_n(x) = 1 \qquad (-\infty < x < \infty).$$

Using the definition of $J_n(x)$ given in Sec. 2 of Chapter 4, we have (formally)

$$\sum_{n=0}^{\infty} \frac{1}{n!} \left(\frac{x}{2}\right)^n J_n(x) = \sum_{n=0}^{\infty} \left[\frac{1}{n!} \left(\frac{x}{2}\right)^n \sum_{k=0}^{\infty} \frac{(-1)^k}{(n+k)!\, k!} \left(\frac{x}{2}\right)^{2k+n} \right]$$

(4) $$= \sum_{n=0}^{\infty} \left[\sum_{k=0}^{\infty} a_{k,n} \right],$$

if we set

$$a_{k,n} = \frac{(-1)^k}{n!\,(n+k)!\,k!} \left(\frac{x}{2}\right)^{2k+2n}.$$

We assert that

(5)
$$(\mathscr{T}) \sum_{k,n=0}^{\infty} a_{k,n} = 1 \,.$$

We have

$$\sum_{(k,n)\in T_i} a_{k,n} = \sum_{j=0}^{i} \sum_{k+n=j} a_{k,n} \,.$$

Now

$$\sum_{k+n=j} a_{k,n} = \frac{1}{j!} \left(\frac{x}{2}\right)^{2j} \sum_{k+n=j} \frac{(-1)^k}{n!k!}$$

$$= \frac{1}{j!} \left(\frac{x}{2}\right)^{2j} \frac{1}{j!} \sum_{k=0}^{j} \binom{j}{k} (-1)^k$$

$$= \begin{cases} 1 & (j=0) \\ 0 & (j=1, 2, \cdots) \,, \end{cases}$$

and from this **(5)** follows. In view of **(4)** and **(5)** our demonstration would be complete if we knew that

(6)
$$\sum_{n=0}^{\infty} \left[\sum_{k=0}^{\infty} a_{k,n} \right] = (\mathscr{T}) \sum_{k,n=0}^{\infty} a_{k,n} \,.$$

By Theorem 4b it is enough to show that

(7)
$$(\mathscr{T}) \sum_{k,n=0}^{\infty} |a_{k,n}| < \infty \,.$$

Since
$$\sum_{k+n=j} |a_{k,n}| = \frac{x^{2j}}{j!\,j!\,2^j} \,,$$

the relation **(7)** is equivalent to

$$\sum_{j=0}^{\infty} \frac{x^{2j}}{j!\,j!\,2^j} < \infty$$

which is valid for all x ($-\infty < x < \infty$). Thus **(7)** holds, and our proof is complete.

PROBLEMS

1. Prove that for $-\infty < x < \infty$,

$$\sum_{n=0}^{\infty} \frac{1}{n!} \left(\frac{x}{2}\right)^{n+1} J_{n+1}(x) = \left(\frac{x}{2}\right)^2 .$$

2. Prove that for $|x| < \pi$,

$$- \log \left(\frac{\sin x}{x}\right) = \sum_{n=1}^{\infty} \left(\frac{x}{\pi}\right)^{2n} \frac{\zeta(2n)}{n} .$$

HINT: By problem 13 of Sec. 2, Chapter 4, if $|x| < \pi$, then

$$\log \left(\frac{\sin x}{x}\right) = \sum_{k=1}^{\infty} \log \left(1 - \frac{x^2}{k^2 \pi^2}\right) .$$

Expand each log term on the right in a Maclaurin series, etc.

3. Prove that

$$\sum_{n=0}^{\infty} \frac{2^n x^{2^n}}{1 + x^{2^n}} = \frac{x}{1-x} \qquad (|x| < 1)$$

by expanding each term on the left in a Maclaurin series and suitably regrouping.

5. Summability

Let \mathscr{S} satisfy the conditions of **(3)** of Sec. 1, and let us define

$$l_{i,n} = \begin{cases} 1 & (n \in S_i) \\ 0 & (n \notin S_i) . \end{cases}$$

Then the ith generalized partial sum σ_i satisfies

(1) $$\sigma_i = \sum_{n \in S_i} a_n = \sum_{n=0}^{\infty} l_{i,n} a_n$$

and thus

(2) $$(\mathscr{S}) \sum_{n=0}^{\infty} a_n = \lim_{i \to \infty} \sum_{n=0}^{\infty} l_{i,n} a_n .$$

Notice that because of Condition 1 of **(3)** of Sec. 1, the formally infinite sums on the right of **(1)** and **(2)** are really finite. The following evident generalization

of (**2**) suggests itself. Let $\lambda_{i,n}$ be an (arbitrary) function on $\mathfrak{P} \times \mathfrak{P}$ satisfying the condition

(**3**) $\{n \mid \lambda_{i,n} \neq 0\}$ is finite for each $i \in \mathfrak{P}$.

We define

(**4**) $$(\varLambda) \sum_{0}^{\infty} a_n = \lim_{i \to \infty} \sum_{n=0}^{\infty} \lambda_{i,n}\, a_n$$

if this limit exists. Note that because of the condition (**3**), the sum on the right of (**4**) is finite[1] for each i. Without further conditions on the λ's we cannot expect that the process $(\varLambda) \sum_{n=0}^{\infty} a_n$ will have the property established in Sec. 1 for $(\mathscr{S}) \sum_{n=0}^{\infty} a_n$, that $(\mathscr{S}) \sum_{n=0}^{\infty} a_n = \sum_{n=0}^{\infty} a_n$ whenever $\sum_{n=0}^{\infty} a_n$ is absolutely convergent.

THEOREM 5a. Let $\lambda_{i,n}$ satisfy the conditions:

1. $\lim\limits_{i \to \infty} \lambda_{i,n} = 1$ $(n \in \mathfrak{P})$;

2. there is a constant M such that $\mid \lambda_{i,n} \mid \leq M$ for $(i,n) \in \mathfrak{P} \times \mathfrak{P}$;

then $$(\varLambda) \sum_{0}^{\infty} a_n = \sum_{0}^{\infty} a_n$$

whenever $\sum_{0}^{\infty} a_n$ converges absolutely.

Note that if the constants $\lambda_{i,n} = l_{i,n}$ arise from a family of generalized partial sums \mathscr{S}, Conditions ii and iii of (**3**), Sec. 1, imply that Condition 1 above is satisfied. Condition 2 above is of course satisfied with $M = 1$. Thus Theorem 5a implies Theorem 1e as a special case.

Proof. Let $\epsilon > 0$ be given. Choose $\delta > 0$ so that $(M + 2)\,\delta < \epsilon$. We next choose n_0 so large that $\sum_{n_0+1}^{\infty} \mid a_n \mid < \delta$. Let $\sum_{0}^{\infty} a_n = s$. We have

$$\sum_{n=0}^{\infty} \lambda_{i,n}\, a_n = \sum_{n=0}^{n_0} \lambda_{i,n}\, a_n + \sum_{n=n_0+1}^{\infty} \lambda_{i,n}\, a_n,$$

$$\sum_{n=0}^{\infty} \lambda_{i,n}\, a_n - s = \sum_{n=0}^{n_0} (\lambda_{i,n} - 1)\, a_n + \sum_{n=n_0+1}^{\infty} (\lambda_{i,n} - 1)\, a_n .$$

Since $\mid \lambda_{i,n} - 1 \mid \leq M + 1$ for all i and n, we have

$$\mid \sum_{n=n_0+1}^{\infty} (\lambda_{i,n} - 1)\, a_i \mid \leq \sum_{n=n_0+1}^{\infty} (M + 1)\mid a_n \mid \leq (M + 1)\,\delta .$$

[1] The condition (3) is not really necessary and can be dispensed with at the cost of some additional complications in our demonstrations.

Condition 1 implies that $\lim_{i\to\infty} (\lambda_{i,n} - 1) = 0$ for $0 \le n \le n_0$. Theorems 1b and 1c of Chapter 1 now imply that

$$\lim_{i\to\infty} \sum_{n=0}^{n_0} (\lambda_{i,n} - 1) a_n = 0 \,.$$

Thus there is an index i_0 so large that

$$\left| \sum_{n=0}^{n_0} (\lambda_{i,n} - 1) a_n \right| \le \delta \qquad \text{if } i \ge i_0 \,.$$

Combining these results, we see that

$$\left| \sum_{n=0}^{\infty} \lambda_{i,n} a_n - s \right| \le (M + 1) \delta + \delta < \epsilon \qquad \text{if } i \ge i_0 \,,$$

and our proof is complete.

The Conditions 1 and 2 of Theorem 5a are not only sufficient but necessary as well. Suppose that the process (\varLambda), subject only to (3), has the property that

$$(\varLambda) \sum_{n=0}^{\infty} a_n = \sum_{n=0}^{\infty} a_n$$

whenever the latter series is absolutely convergent. Take any $m \in \mathfrak{P}$, and define a_n as 0 if $n \ne m$ and a_m as 1. Then $\sum_{n=0}^{\infty} a_n = 1$, the series converging absolutely. By assumption

$$\lim_{i\to\infty} \sum_{n=0}^{\infty} \lambda_{i,n} a_n = 1 \,.$$

But since here

$$\sum_{n=0}^{\infty} \lambda_{i,n} a_n = \lambda_{i,m} \,,$$

it follows that

$$\lim_{i\to\infty} \lambda_{i,m} = 1 \,.$$

Since this is true for each $m \in \mathfrak{P}$, we have established the necessity of Condition 1. The proof that Condition 2 is necessary is carried out by showing that if it is not satisfied, we can construct a series $\sum_{n=0}^{\infty} a_n$ which is absolutely convergent but for which $\lim_{i\to\infty} \sum_{n=0}^{\infty} \lambda_{i,n} a_n$ does not converge. This construction is very simple using the methods of modern functional analysis, but by the elementary methods available to us it is long and is omitted.

It is often convenient to replace the formula

$$\sigma_i = \sum_{n=0}^{\infty} \lambda_{i,n}\, a_n$$

by an equivalent formula for σ_i in terms of the partial sums $s_n = \sum_{k=0}^{n} a_k$. Let us set

(5) $\Lambda_{i,n} = \lambda_{i,n} - \lambda_{i,n+1}$

By Lemma 4a of Chapter 4 we then have

(6) $$\sigma_i = \sum_{n=0}^{\infty} \Lambda_{i,n}\, s_n\,.$$

Because of **(3)** this summation is again only formally infinite.

EXAMPLE 1. The summability process which will be of greatest importance to us is Cesàro summability of order 1 defined by

$$\lambda_{i,n}^{(1)} = \begin{cases} 1 - \dfrac{n}{i+1} & (0 \le n \le i) \\ 0 & (n > i)\,, \end{cases}$$

or equivalently

$$\Lambda_{i,n}^{(1)} = \begin{cases} \dfrac{1}{i+1} & (0 \le n \le i) \\ 0 & (n > i)\,. \end{cases}$$

The symbol $(C,1)$ will be used to designate this process.

It is evident that the constants $\lambda_{i,n}^{(1)}$ satisfy the conditions of Theorem 5a, and thus if $\sum_{n=0}^{\infty} a_n = a$, the series converging absolutely, then

(7) $$(C,1) \sum_{n=0}^{\infty} a_n = a\,.$$

Actually the $(C,1)$ process has, as we shall show in Sec. 6, the stronger property that **(7)** holds whenever the series $\sum_0^{\infty} a_n$ converges; that is, the convergence need not be absolute.

PROBLEMS

1. Show that $(C,1) \sum_{n=0}^{\infty} (-1)^n = \frac{1}{2}$. HINT: Use formula **(6)**.

Let, for $0 < \alpha < \infty$,

$$\lambda_{i,n}^{(\alpha)} = \binom{i-n+\alpha}{i-n} \div \binom{i+\alpha}{i} \qquad (n = 0, 1, \cdots, i)$$

$$= 0 \qquad (n > i).$$

The corresponding summability process is called (C,α) summability or Cesàro summability of order α.

2. Verify that $\lambda_{i,n}^{(1)}$ as defined above coincides with $\lambda_{i,n}^{(1)}$ as defined in Example 1.

3. Show that

$$\lambda_{i,n}^{(\alpha)} = \frac{i}{i+\alpha} \cdot \frac{i-1}{i+\alpha-1} \cdots \frac{i-n+1}{i+\alpha-n+1}$$

and deduce that

$$\lim_{i \to \infty} \lambda_{i,n}^{(\alpha)} = 1 \qquad (n \in \mathfrak{P}).$$

4. Show that

$$\lambda_{i,n+1}^{(\alpha)} = \lambda_{i,n}^{(\alpha)} \left(\frac{i-n}{i+\alpha-n} \right),$$

and use this to prove

$$1 = \lambda_{i,0}^{(\alpha)} > \lambda_{i,1}^{(\alpha)} > \cdots \lambda_{i,i}^{(\alpha)} > 0.$$

Note that Problems 3 and 4 together show that the summability method (C,α) satisfies the assumptions of Theorem 5a.

Let p_k $(k = 0, 1, \cdots)$ be nonnegative numbers[1] such that $\sum_{k=0}^{\infty} p_k = \infty$. We define

$$\pi_{i,n} = \frac{p_n + p_{n+1} + \cdots + p_i}{p_0 + p_1 + \cdots + p_i} \qquad (0 \le n \le i)$$

$$= 0 \qquad (n > i).$$

The corresponding summability method is called the Norlünd method associated with the constants $\{p_k\}_0^\infty$. If $\lim_{i \to \infty} \sum_{n=0}^{\infty} \pi_{i,n} a_n = a$, we write $(N_\pi) \sum_0^\infty a_n = a$.

5. Show that if $p_k = 1$ $(k = 0, 1, \cdots)$, then N_π reduces to Cesàro summability of order 1.

6. Prove that for the general Norlünd process:

(a) $\lim_{i \to \infty} \pi_{i,n} = 1$ $\quad (n \in \mathfrak{P})$;

(b) $1 = \pi_{i,0} \ge \pi_{i,1} \ge \pi_{i,i} \ge 0$.

Problem 6 shows that every Nörlund method N_π satisfies the assumptions of Theorem 5a.

[1] In order to avoid irrelevant difficulties, we shall also assume that $p_0 > 0$.

7. Prove that if

$$\lim_{i \to \infty} \frac{\sum_{2k \le i} p_{2k}}{\sum_{k \le i} p_k} = r \,,$$

then

$$(N_\pi) \sum_{n=0}^{\infty} (-1)^n = r.$$

6. Regularity

Theorem 5a asserts that if \varLambda is a summability process satisfying Conditions 1 and 2 of Theorem 5a and if $\sum_{n=0}^{\infty} a_n = s$, then $(\varLambda) \sum_{n=0}^{\infty} a_n = s$ at least if $\sum_{n=0}^{\infty} a_n$ converges absolutely. Because of the central importance of (ordinary) convergence it is crucial to know conditions under which this same conclusion will hold with ordinary convergence in place of absolute convergence.

DEFINITION 6a. A summability process \varLambda is said to be *regular* if $(\varLambda) \sum_{n=0}^{\infty} a_n = s$ whenever $\sum_{n=0}^{\infty} a_n = s$.

Because of its particular interest and also because it illustrates the ideas involved without notational complications, we begin with $(C,1)$ summability.

THEOREM 6b. $(C,1)$ summability is regular.

Proof. We have

$$\sigma_i = \frac{s_0 + s_1 + \cdots + s_i}{i + 1} \,,$$

$$\sigma_i - s = \frac{(s_0 - s) + (s_1 - s) + \cdots + (s_i - s)}{i + 1} .$$

Since $\lim_{k \to \infty} s_k = s$, given $\epsilon > 0$ there is an index n_0 such that if $n > n_0$, then $|s - s_n| \le \epsilon/2$. Now

$$| \sigma_i - s | \le \frac{1}{i+1} \sum_{n=0}^{n_0} | s_n - s | + \frac{1}{i+1} \sum_{n=n_0+1}^{i} | s_n - s |.$$

We have

$$\frac{1}{i+1} \sum_{n_0+1}^{i} | s_n - s | \le \frac{i - n_0}{i+1} \cdot \frac{\epsilon}{2} < \frac{\epsilon}{2} .$$

There is an index i_1 such that if $i > i_1$, then

$$\frac{1}{i+1} \sum_{n=0}^{n_0} | s_n - s | < \frac{\epsilon}{2} .$$

It now follows that for $i \geq i_1$, $|\sigma_i - s| < \epsilon$, and thus since ϵ is arbitrary, $\lim_{i \to \infty} \sigma_i = s$.

We now turn to the general case.

THEOREM 6c. If $\lambda_{i,n}$ satisfies the conditions[1]

1. $\lim_{i \to \infty} \lambda_{i,n} = 1 \quad (n \in \mathfrak{P})$;

2. there is a constant M such that $\sum_{n=0}^{\infty} |\lambda_{i,n} - \lambda_{i,n+1}| \leq M$, $i \in \mathfrak{P}$, then Λ is regular.

The assumptions of Theorem 6b are stronger than the assumptions of Theorem 5a, which is natural since they guarantee a stronger conclusion.

Proof. We have

$$ s_i = \sum_{n=0}^{i} a_n, \qquad \sigma_i = \sum_{n=0}^{\infty} \lambda_{i,n} a_n . $$

We must show that $\lim_{i \to \infty} \sigma_i = s$ whenever $\lim_{i \to \infty} s_i = s$. By **(6)** of Sec. 5

$$ \sigma_i = \sum_{n=0}^{\infty} \Lambda_{i,n} s_n $$

where

$$ \Lambda_{i,n} = \lambda_{i,n} - \lambda_{i,n+1} . $$

Since

$$ \sum_{n=0}^{\infty} \Lambda_{i,n} = \lambda_{i,0} , $$

we have

$$ \sigma_i - \lambda_{i,0} s = \sum_{n=0}^{\infty} \Lambda_{i,n}(s_n - s) . $$

Given $\epsilon > 0$, let us choose $\delta > 0$ so that $(M + 2)\delta < \epsilon$. By assumption there is an integer n_0 such that $|s_n - s| < \delta$ if $n \geq n_0$. Now

$$ \sigma_i - \lambda_{i,0} s = \sum_{n=0}^{n_0} \Lambda_{i,n}(s_n - s) + \sum_{n_0+1} \Lambda_{i,n}(s_n - s) , $$

and thus using Condition 2, we have

$$ |\sigma_i - \lambda_{i,0} s| \leq \sum_{n=0}^{n_0} |\Lambda_{i,n}| \, |s_n - s| + M\delta . $$

[1] We also assume that (3) of Sec. 5 is satisfied. However Theorem 6b is true without this assumption.

Now $\lim\limits_{i\to\infty} | \varLambda_{i,n} | = \lim\limits_{i\to\infty} | \lambda_{i,n} - \lambda_{i,n+1} | = 0$ for each $n = 0, 1, \cdots, n_0$ by Condition 1. By Theorems 1b and 1c of Chapter 1

$$\lim_{i\to\infty} \sum_{n=0}^{n_0} | \varLambda_{i,n} | \, | s_n - s | = 0$$

and thus there is an index i_1 such that if $i \geq i_1$, then

$$\sum_{n=0}^{n_0} | \varLambda_{i,n} | \, | s_n - s | < \delta .$$

Thus

$$| \sigma_i - \lambda_{i,0} s | < (M + 1) \, \delta \qquad \text{if } i \leq i_1 .$$

Since $\lim\limits_{i\to\infty} \lambda_{i,0} s = s$ by Condition 1, there is an index i_2 such that $| \lambda_{i,0} s - s | < \delta$ if $i \geq i_2$. Let $i_0 = \max (i_i, i_2)$; then

$$| \sigma_i - s | \leq | \sigma_i - \lambda_{i,0} s | + | \lambda_{i,0} s - s | \leq (M + 2) \, \delta < \epsilon \qquad \text{if } i \geq i_0 .$$

Since ϵ is arbitrary, our theorem is proved.

Conditions 1 and 2 of Theorem 6b are also *necessary* for regularity.

It is sometimes convenient to have the conditions for regularity in terms of the $\varLambda_{i,n}$. The conditions then are:

1. $\lim\limits_{i\to\infty} \sum\limits_{n=0}^{\infty} \varLambda_{i,n} = 1$;

2. $\lim\limits_{i\to\infty} \varLambda_{i,n} = 0, n \in \mathfrak{P}$;

3. there exists a constant M such that $\sum_{n=0}^{\infty} | \varLambda_{i,n} | \leq M$ for $i \in \mathfrak{P}$.

The verification of this equivalence is left to the reader as an exercise.

[6]

Power Series and Real Analytic Functions

1. Radius of Convergence

The first sections of this chapter give a systematic development of the theory of real power series. Some of these results have been established before in special cases. Following this, there is an introduction to the theory of real analytic functions.

The various examples of power series examined in Sec. 9 of Chapter 1 suggest the following result.

THEOREM 1a. With each power series

$$(1) \qquad \sum_{n=0}^{\infty} a_n(x - c)^n$$

there is associated a number r_a $(0 \leq r_a \leq \infty)$ such that the series converges (absolutely) for $|x - c| < r_a$ and diverges for $|x - c| > r_a$. Moreover if $0 \leq r_1 < r_a$, the series converges uniformly for $|x - c| \leq r_1$.

Proof. For the examples mentioned this was established by the ratio test, Theorem 5e of Chapter 1. The general case must be dealt with using different arguments. Let

$$R = \{x \mid \sum_{n=0}^{\infty} a_n(x - c)^n \text{ is convergent}\}.$$

At the end of the proof it will be evident that R must consist of the open interval $|x - c| < r_a$ together with none, one, or both of its end points. However at the beginning of the proof the structure of R is unknown. Let

$$r_a = \operatorname*{l.u.b.}_{x \in R} |x - c|.$$

We shall prove that r_a has the asserted properties. It is evident from the definition of r_a that the series (1) diverges if $|x - c| > r_a$. Choose r_1 $(0 \leq r_1 < r_a)$. By the definition of R there exists $x_1 \in R$ such that $r_1 < |x_1 - c|$. Since $\sum_{n=0}^{\infty} a_n(x_1 - c)^n$ converges $a_n(x_1 - c)^n \to 0$ as $n \to \infty$ (by Theorem 3d of Chapter 1); a fortiori there exists a constant M such that

$$(2) \qquad |a_n| \cdot |x_1 - c|^n \leq M \qquad (n = 0, 1, \cdots).$$

131

If $|x - c| \leq r_1$, then

$$|a_n| \cdot |x - c|^n \leq r_1^n |x_1 - c|^{-n} |x_1 - c|^n |a_n|$$
$$\leq r_1^n |x_1 - c|^{-n} M$$
$$\leq \rho^n M$$

where $\rho = r_1 |x_1 - c|^{-1}$ so that $0 \leq \rho < 1$. By the Weierstrass comparison test, Theorem 2h of Chapter 4, the series (1) converges absolutely and uniformly for $|x - c| \leq r_1$. Finally since r_1 is arbitrary subject to the restriction $0 \leq r_1 < r_a$, the series (1) is seen to converge absolutely for $|x - c| < r_a$. The number r_a is called the *radius of convergence* of the series (1). Let us set

(3)
$$A(x) = \sum_{n=0}^{\infty} a_n(x - c)^n \qquad (|x - c| < r_a).$$

THEOREM 1b. The function $A(x)$ defined by (3) is continuous for $|x - c| < r_a$.

Proof. Consider any x_1 satisfying $|x_1 - c| < r_a$, and choose r_1 so that $|x_1 - c| < r_1 < r_a$. By Theorem 1a the series (1) converges uniformly for $|x - c| \leq r_1$. The terms of this series are continuous functions of x. Therefore by Theorem 2e of Chapter 4, $A(x)$ restricted to $|x - c| \leq r_1$ is continuous, and in particular $A(x)$ is continuous at x_1.

The following result gives a formula for the radius of convergence of a power series in terms of the coefficients. Although this formula will not be needed later, it is of some interest. Familiarity is assumed with the material on limit superior contained in Sec. 1 of the Appendix.

THEOREM 1c. The radius of convergence r_a of the power series $\sum_{n=0}^{\infty} a_n(x - c)^n$ is given by

$$\frac{1}{r_a} = \overline{\lim_{n \to \infty}} |a_n|^{1/n}.$$

Proof. If $\overline{\lim_{n \to \infty}} |a_n|^{1/n}$ is ∞ (or 0), then r_a is to be taken as 0 (or ∞). We shall carry out the demonstration on the assumption that $\overline{\lim_{n \to \infty}} |a_n|^{1/n} = \alpha$ is finite and strictly positive. Let $\epsilon > 0$. Then for all sufficiently large n, $|a_n|^{1/n} \leq \alpha + \epsilon$, or equivalently $|a_n| \leq (\alpha + \epsilon)^n$. Thus if $|x - c| < (\alpha + \epsilon)^{-1}$ so that $\rho = (\alpha + \epsilon) |x - c|$ is less than 1, then for all sufficiently large n,

$$|a_n| \cdot |x - c|^n \leq |x - c|^n (\alpha + \epsilon)^n = \rho^n.$$

By the comparison test, Theorem 5a of Chapter 1, the series $\sum_{n=0}^{\infty} a_n(x - c)^n$ converges (absolutely) for $|x - c| < (\alpha + \epsilon)^{-1}$, and thus since ϵ is arbitrary, $r_a \geq 1/\alpha$. Next let $\epsilon > 0$ be so small that $\alpha - \epsilon > 0$. Then for infinitely many n,

$|a_n|^{1/n} > (\alpha - \epsilon)$, or equivalently $|a_n| \geq (\alpha - \epsilon)^n$. Thus if $|x - c| > (\alpha - \epsilon)^{-1}$, then for infinitely many n,

$$|a_n| |x - c|^n > |x - c|^n (\alpha - \epsilon)^{-n} > 1.$$

Thus by Corollary 3e of Chapter 1 the series $\sum_{n=0}^{\infty} a_n(x - c)^n$ diverges if $|x - c| > (\alpha - \epsilon)^{-1}$, or since ϵ is arbitrary, $r_a \leq 1/\alpha$.

EXAMPLE 1. Determine the radius of convergence of the series

(4)
$$\sum_{n=0}^{\infty} \mu(n) x^n$$

where $\mu(n)$ is the Möbius function defined in Sec. 3 of Chapter 5. The ratio test cannot be applied since the limit in question does not exist. On the other hand it is evident that

$$\overline{\lim_{n \to \infty}} |\mu(n)|^{1/n} = 1$$

so that the radius of convergence of the series (4) is 1.

PROBLEMS

Let $0 \leq \lambda_1 < \lambda_2 \cdots$, $\lim_{n \to \infty} \lambda_n = \infty$. A series of the form

(5)
$$\sum_{n=1}^{\infty} b_n e^{-\lambda_n s}$$

is called a "generalized Dirichlet series."

1. Show that corresponding to the series (5), there exists a number γ_a, the *abscissa of absolute convergence*, such that the series converges absolutely for $s > \gamma_a$ and does not converge absolutely for $s < \gamma_a$.

2. Show that if the $\{\lambda_n\}_1^{\infty}$ have the property that for some $\epsilon > 0$ the series

(6)
$$\sum_1^{\infty} e^{-\epsilon \lambda_n}$$

is convergent, then the series (5) diverges for $s < \gamma_a - \epsilon$. In particular if (6) holds for every $\epsilon > 0$, the series (5) diverges for $s < \gamma_a$.

2. Operations on Power Series

Given one or more power series, we may construct from them new power series in various ways. For example, we may differentiate a given power series term by term. It is then natural to ask what is the radius of convergence of the

new series and how is its sum related to the sum of the original series. In this section we shall study these questions for a variety of basic operations. Much of this material has been treated before in special cases. The treatment here is general and systematic.

THEOREM 2a. Let the series

$$(1) \qquad \sum_{n=0}^{\infty} a_n(x - c)^n$$

have radius of convergence r, and let $A(x)$ be the sum of the series (1) for $|x - c| < r$. Consider the series

$$(2) \qquad \sum_{n=0}^{\infty} \frac{1}{n+1} a_n(x - c)^{n+1}$$

[obtained by formal term by term integration of (1)]. Let r_{-1} be the radius of convergence of the series (2), and let $A_{-1}(x)$ be its sum for $|x - c| < r_{-1}$. Then the following relations hold:

1. $r_{-1} = r$;
2. $A_{-1}(x) = \int_c^x A(u)\, du$ \qquad for $|x - c| < r$.

Proof. By Theorem 1a the series (1) converges uniformly for $|x - c| \leq r_1$ for any $0 < r_1 < r$. Applying Theorem 2f of Chapter 4, we see that the series (2) converges for $|x - c| \leq r_1$ and that $A_{-1}(x) = \int_c^x A(u)\, du$ for $|x - c| \leq r_1$. Since r_1 is any number satisfying $0 < r_1 < r$, it follows that Relation 2 is valid and in particular that the series (2) converges for $|x - c| < r$. This implies that $r_{-1} \geq r$; it remains only to show that $r_{-1} > r$ is impossible. Suppose that $r_{-1} > r$. Choose x_1 and x_2 so that $r < |x_1 - c| < |x_2 - c| < r_{-1}$. Since $|x_2 - c| < r_{-1}$, the series

$$\sum_{n=0}^{\infty} \frac{1}{n+1} a_n(x_2 - c)^{n+1}$$

is convergent. By a now familiar argument this implies that there exists a constant M such that

$$\frac{1}{n+1} |a_n| \cdot |x_2 - c|^{n+1} \leq M \qquad (n = 0, 1, \cdots)$$

or \qquad $|a_n| \leq M(n+1) |x_2 - c|^{-n-1} \qquad (n = 0, 1, \cdots)$.

Let $\rho = |x_1 - c| / |x_2 - c|$ and $M_1 = M / |x_2 - c|$. We have

$$|a_n| |x_1 - c|^n \leq M(n+1) |x_2 - c|^{-n-1} |x_1 - c|^n = M_1(n+1) \rho^n.$$

Since $0 < \rho < 1$, the series $\sum_0^\infty M_1(n+1)\rho^n$ is convergent by the ratio test, and therefore by the comparison test so is the series $\sum_0^\infty a_n(x_1 - c)^n$. But since $|x_1 - c| > r$, this is a contradiction. Thus $r_{-1} = r$.

THEOREM 2b. With the above notations consider the series

(3)
$$\sum_{n=0}^{\infty} na_n(x-c)^{n-1}$$

[obtained by formal term by term differentiation of (1)]. Let r_1 be the radius of convergence of the series (3), and let $A_1(x)$ be its sum for $|x - c| < r_1$. Then the following relations hold:

1. $r_1 = r$;

2. $A_1(x) = \dfrac{d}{dx} A(x)$ for $|x - c| < r$.

 Proof. If the series (3) is formally integrated term by term, we obtain the series

$$\sum_{n=1}^{\infty} a_n(x-c)^n .$$

Now apply Theorem 2a.

COROLLARY 2c. Given a power series

$$\sum_{n=0}^{\infty} a_n(x-c)^n$$

with positive radius of convergence $r > 0$, let $A(x)$ be its sum for $|x - c| < r$. Then $A(x)$ is infinitely differentiable for $|x - c| < r$ and

(4)
$$a_m = \frac{1}{m!} A^{(m)}(x) \mid_{x=c} \qquad (m = 0, 1, \cdots) .$$

 Proof. Repeated application of Theorem 2b shows that

$$A^{(m)}(x) = \sum_{n=0}^{\infty} a_n n(n-1) \cdots (n-m+1)(x-c)^{n-m} \qquad (|x-c| < r) .$$

Setting $x = c$, we obtain our desired result. An alternative statement of this result is that every power series with positive radius of convergence is the Taylor series of its sum.

Using Corollary 2c, we can answer the following natural question: Can we have two different power series with center c

$$\sum_{n=0}^{\infty} a_n(x - c)^n \quad \text{and} \quad \sum_{n=0}^{\infty} b_n(x - c)^n$$

which are equal in an interval containing c in its interior? Formula (4) shows that the answer is no!

We turn to algebraic operations on power series. Let

$$\sum_{n=0}^{\infty} a_n(x - c)^n \quad \text{and} \quad \sum_{n=0}^{\infty} b_n(x - c)^n$$

be two power series with center c. Let r_a and r_b be the radii of convergence of these series, and let

(5)
$$A_a(x) = \sum_{n=0}^{\infty} a_n(x - c)^n \quad \text{for } | x - c | < r_a$$

$$A_b(x) = \sum_{n=0}^{\infty} b_n(x - c)^n \quad \text{for } | x - c | < r_b .$$

Let α and β be constants, and consider the series

(6)
$$\sum_{n=0}^{\infty} (\alpha a_n + \beta b_n) (x - c)^n .$$

Formally the series (6) is a linear combination with constants α and β of the two given series. Let r_s be the radius of convergence of the series (6), and let $A_s(x)$ be the sum of the series (6) for $| x - c | < r_s$.

THEOREM 2d. With the above notations, the following relations are valid:

1. $r_s \geq \min\{r_a, r_b\}$;
2. $A_s(x) = \alpha A_a(x) + \beta A_b(x)$ for $| x - c | < \min\{r_a, r_b\}$.

Proof. This follows immediately from Theorem 3b of Chapter 1.
Let us also consider

(7)
$$\sum_{n=0}^{\infty} \left(\sum_{k=0}^{n} a_{n-k} b_k \right) (x - c)^n .$$

Let r_p be the radius of convergence of the series (7), and let $A_p(x)$ be the sum of the series (7) for $| x - c | < r_p$.

THEOREM 2e. With the above notations the following relations are valid:

1. $r_p \geq \min\{r_a, r_b\}$;
2. $A_p(x) = A_a(x) A_b(x)$ for $|x - c| < \min\{r_a, r_b\}$.

Proof. It is shown in Sec 3 of Chapter 5 that if for a given value of x both series in (5) are absolutely convergent, the series (7) is also (absolutely) convergent, and $A_p(x) = A_a(x) A_b(x)$. This fact together with Theorem 1a gives us our result.

Consider the series

$$\text{(8)} \qquad \sum_{n=0}^{\infty} d_n(x - c)^n \qquad \text{where } d_0 \neq 0.$$

We assert that there exists a series

$$\text{(9)} \qquad \sum_{n=0}^{\infty} e_n(x - c)^n$$

such that the formal product of (8) and (9) is

$$\text{(10)} \qquad 1 + 0(x - c) + 0(x - c)^2 + \cdots.$$

If (10) is to hold, the coefficients of the series (9) must satisfy the infinite system of equations:

$$d_0 e_0 = 1,$$
$$d_0 e_1 + d_1 e_0 = 0,$$
$$\text{(11)} \qquad d_0 e_2 + d_1 e_1 + d_2 e_0 = 0,$$
$$\vdots$$
$$d_0 e_m + d_1 e_{m-1} + \cdots + d_m e_0 = 0,$$
$$\vdots$$

Because of the special form of these equations and because we have assumed $d_0 \neq 0$, these equations have a unique solution; in fact

$$e_0 = d_0^{-1},$$
$$e_1 = - d_1 d_0^{-2},$$
$$e_2 = (d_2 d_0 - d_1^2) d_0^{-3}, \text{ etc.}$$

The series (9) will be called the formal multiplicative inverse of the series (8).

THEOREM 2f. Let the series (8) where $d_0 \neq 0$ have radius of convergence r_d where $r_d > 0$, and let $A_d(x)$ be the sum of (8) for $|x - c| < r_d$. Let (9) be the series which is the formal multiplicative inverse of (8). Let r_e be the radius of

convergence of the series (**9**), and let $A_e(x)$ be the sum of (**9**) for $|x - c| < r_e$. Under these assumptions we have:

 1. $r_e > 0$;

 2. $A_d(x)\, A_e(x) = 1$ for $|x - c| < \min\{r_d, r_e\}$.

Proof. We begin by showing that $r_e > 0$. Let us choose $\rho > 0$ sufficiently small for the condition

$$\textbf{(12)} \qquad \sum_{n=1}^{\infty} \rho^n \, |d_n| \leq d_0$$

to hold. We assert that

$$\textbf{(13)} \qquad |e_n| \leq |d_0|^{-1} \rho^{-n} \qquad (n = 0, 1, \cdots).$$

We proceed by induction. Since $e_0 = d_0^{-1}$, (**13**) is true for $n = 0$. Suppose that (**13**) holds for $n = 0, 1, \cdots, m - 1$. We shall show that it holds for $n = m$. By (**11**)

$$d_0\, e_m = -\, d_1\, e_{m-1} - d_2\, e_{m-2} - \cdots - d_m\, e_0\,.$$

Using our induction assumption and (**12**), we find that

$$|d_0|\,|e_m| \leq |d_1|\,|d_0|^{-1}\rho^{-m+1} + |d_2|\,|d_0|^{-1}\rho^{-m+2} + \cdots + |d_m|\,|d_0|^{-1}$$
$$\leq |d_0|^{-1}\rho^{-m}\{|d_1|\,\rho + |d_2|\,\rho^2 + \cdots + |d_m|\,\rho^m\}$$
$$\leq |d_0|^{-1}\rho^{-m}\,|d_0| = \rho^m,$$

from which it follows that $|e_m| \leq |d_0|^{-1}\rho^{-m}$ as desired. Since (**13**) implies that $r_e \geq \rho$, our assertion that $r_e > 0$ has been proved, and in addition we have obtained a useful lower bound for r_e. To obtain Conclusion 2, we have now only to apply Theorem 2e.

 EXAMPLE 1. Compute the series which is the formal multiplicative inverse of the series

$$\sum_{0}^{\infty} \frac{x^n}{(n+1)!}\,.$$

This series is equal to $(e^x - 1)/x$ if $x \neq 0$ and to 1 if $x = 0$. If $\sum_{0}^{\infty} b_n\, x^n$ is the desired series, we must have

$$1b_0 = 1,$$
$$1b_1 + \tfrac{1}{2}b_0 = 0,$$
$$1b_2 + \tfrac{1}{2}b_1 + \tfrac{1}{6}b_0 = 0,$$
$$1b_3 + \tfrac{1}{2}b_2 + \tfrac{1}{6}b_1 + \tfrac{1}{24}b_0 = 0,$$
$$\vdots$$

from which it follows that

$$b_0 = 1, b_1 = -\tfrac{1}{2}, b_2 = \tfrac{1}{12}, b_3 = 0, \cdots .$$

There is here no simple rule for the formation of the successive b_n's. The radius of convergence r_b of the series $\sum_0^\infty b_n x^n$ cannot be found by elementary methods.[1] However by Theorem 2e, $r_b \geq \rho$ if ρ is any number for which

$$\sum_1^\infty \frac{\rho^n}{(n+1)!} \leq 1.$$

Since

$$\sum_1^\infty \frac{1^n}{(n+1)!} = e - 1 - 1 = 0.71828 \cdots \leq 1,$$

it follows at least that $r_b \geq 1$.

The series $\sum_0^\infty b_n x^n$, the first few terms of which were computed above, lends itself to an extremely interesting application. Let N be a positive integer. Starting from the identity $(y^N - 1)/(y - 1) = 1 + y + y^2 + \cdots + y^{N-1}$, it is easy to deduce that

(14) $\qquad (e^{Nx} - 1) \cdot \dfrac{x}{e^x - 1} = x \sum_{j=0}^{N-1} e^{jx} \qquad (-\infty < x < \infty)$

where $x/(e^x - 1)$ is defined as 1 for $x = 0$. Let us compute the coefficient of x^m in the power series expansion about $x = 0$ of

$$(e^{Nx} - 1) \frac{x}{e^x - 1} .$$

Since $\qquad\qquad e^{Nx} - 1 = \displaystyle\sum_{n=1}^\infty \frac{N^n}{n!} x^n,$

we find that the coefficient of x^m is

$$\sum_{k=1}^m \frac{N^k}{k!} b_{m-k} .$$

On the other hand, the coefficient of x^m in the power series expansion about $x = 0$ of

$$x[1 + e^x + e^{2x} + \cdots + e^{(N-1)x}]$$

[1] Using the theory of complex analytic functions, it is easily proved that $r_b = 2\pi$.

is if $(m \geq 1)$,

$$\sum_{j=1}^{N-1} \frac{j^{m-1}}{(m-1)!} .$$

Equating these expressions, we have proved that

(15) $$\sum_{j=0}^{N-1} j^{m-1} = \sum_{k=1}^{m} N^k \, b_{m-k} \frac{(m-1)!}{k!} .$$

If, for example, we take $m = 2$ in **(15)**, we obtain the identity

$$0 + 1 + 2 + \cdots + N - 1 = \tfrac{1}{2}N^2 - \tfrac{1}{2}N .$$

If we take $m = 3$, we obtain

$$0^2 + 1^2 + 2^2 + \cdots + (N-1)^2 = \tfrac{1}{3}N^3 - \tfrac{1}{2}N^2 + \tfrac{1}{6}N, \text{ etc.}$$

PROBLEMS

1. Give an example in which in Theorem 2d, $r_s = \min\{r_a, r_b\}$ holds and one in which $r_s > \min\{r_a, r_b\}$ holds.

2. Give an example in which in Theorem 2e, $r_p = \min\{r_a, r_b\}$ holds and one in which $r_p > \min\{r_a, r_b\}$ holds.

3. Give an example in which in Theorem 2f, $r_e = \rho$ where ρ is the unique positive number for which $\sum_1^\infty d_n \, \rho^n = d_0$ and one in which $r_e > \rho$.

4. Compute b_4 and b_5 in Example 1. Using these, obtain formulas for the sums

$$\sum_{j=0}^{N-1} j^4 \quad \text{and} \quad \sum_{j=0}^{N-1} j^5 .$$

3. End-point Behavior

Let

(1) $$\sum_{n=0}^{\infty} a_n(x - c)^n$$

be a power series with radius of convergence r_a. Let

(2) $$R_a = \left\{ x \,\Big|\, \sum_{n=0}^{\infty} a_n(x - c)^n \text{ converges} \right\}.$$

The set R_a consists of the points $|x - c| < r_a$ together with none, one, or both of the points $c + r_a, \, c - r_a$.

We can set[1]

(3)
$$A(x) = \sum_{n=0}^{\infty} a_n(x - c)^n \qquad (x \in R_a)$$

instead of merely for $|x - a| < r_a$. By Theorem 2b the function $A(x)$ is continuous for $|x - c| < r_a$. In the present section we shall prove that $A(x)$ is also continuous at $c + r_a$ and $c - r_a$ whenever these points are in R_a.

LEMMA 3a. With the above notations, if $c + r_a(c - r_a) \in R_a$, the series **(1)** converges uniformly for $c \le x \le c + r_a(c - r_a \le x \le c)$.

Proof. Suppose that $c + r_a \in R_a$. By assumption the series

$$\sum_{n=0}^{\infty} a'_n \qquad a'_n = a_n\, r_a^n$$

converges. Let $\alpha_n(x) = (x - c)^n\, r_a^{-n}$ $(n = 0, 1, \cdots)$.
Then if $c \le x \le c + r_a$, we have

$$1 \ge \alpha_0(x) \ge \alpha_1(x) \ge \alpha_2(x) \ge \cdots \ge 0 .$$

By Theorem 4d of Chapter 4 the series

$$\sum_{n=0}^{\infty} a'_n\, \alpha_n(x) = \sum_{n=0}^{\infty} a_n(x - c)^n$$

converges uniformly for $c \le x \le c + r_a$ as was asserted.

THEOREM 3b. (Abel.) The function $A(x)$ defined above is continuous for $x \in R_a$.

Proof. Because of Theorem 1b we need only show that $A(x)$ is continuous at $c + r_a$ and or $c - r_a$ if one or both of these points belongs to R_a. This however is an immediate consequence of Lemma 3a and Theorem 2e of Chapter 4.

Given a series $\sum_{n=0}^{\infty} c_n$, let us write

(4)
$$(A) \sum_{n=0}^{\infty} c_n = s$$

if

(5)
$$\lim_{x \to 1-} \sum_{n=0}^{\infty} c_n\, x^n = s.$$

[1] Strictly speaking the function $A(x)$ defined in Sec. 1 is a restriction of the function $A(x)$ defined above.

In this case the series $\sum_0^\infty c_n$ is said to be *Abel* summable to the value s. The following result asserts that Abel summability is regular. (See Sec. 6 of Chapter 5.)

THEOREM 3c. If $\sum_{n=0}^\infty c_n = s$, then $(A) \sum_{n=0}^\infty c_n = s$.

Proof. Since by assumption $\sum_0^\infty c_n$ converges, it follows that $\lim_{n\to\infty} c_n = 0$ and a fortiori that there exists a constant M such that $|c_n| \le M$ $(n = 0, 1, \cdots)$. Consequently $r_c \ge 1$, and

$$C(x) = \sum_{n=0}^\infty c_n x^n$$

converges for $-1 < x < 1$. Since $\sum_0^\infty c_n = s$, the point $x = 1$ also belongs to R_c and $C(1) = s$. By Theorem 3b, $C(x)$ is continuous for $x \in R_c$, and thus $\lim_{x\to 1-} C(x) = C(1) = s$. But this is what we were to show.

Let $0 < x_0 < x_1 < x_2 < \cdots < 1$, and let $\lim_{i\to\infty} x_i = 1$. We set for $i = 0$, $1, 2, \cdots$,

$$\lambda_{i,n} = x_i^n \qquad (n = 0, 1, 2, \cdots).$$

It is evident that

1. $\lim_{i\to\infty} \lambda_{i,n} = 1 \qquad (n = 0, 1, \cdots)$.

Since $1 = x_i^0 = \lambda_{i,0} > x_i^1 = \lambda_{i,1} > \cdots$, and since $\lim_{n\to\infty} \lambda_{i,n} = \lim_{n\to\infty} x_i^n = 0$, we have

2. $\sum_{n=0}^\infty |\lambda_{i,n} - \lambda_{i,n+1}| = 1 \qquad (i = 0, 1, \cdots)$.

By Theorem 6c of Chapter 5 it follows that if $\sum_0^\infty c_n = s$, then

$$\lim_{i\to\infty} \sum_{n=0}^\infty \lambda_{i,n} c_n = s.$$

However inserting the definition of the $\lambda_{i,n}$'s, we can rewrite this as

$$\lim_{i\to\infty} \sum_{n=0}^\infty c_n x_i^n = s.$$

Since the sequence $\{x_i\}_0^\infty$ was arbitrary, a simple argument (left to the reader) shows that

$$\lim_{x\to 1-} \sum_{n=0}^\infty c_n x^n = s.$$

We have thus obtained a second proof[1] of Theorem 3c.

[1] We require the fact that Theorem 6c of Chapter 5 is true without condition (3) Sec. 5 of Chapter 5. Since we have only asserted (but not proved) that Theorem 6c of Chapter 5 is true without this condition, our second proof is not quite complete.

PROBLEMS

1. Prove that if the generalized Dirichlet series

$$(6) \qquad \sum_{n=1}^{\infty} b_n e^{-\lambda_n s}$$

converges, not necessarily absolutely for $s = s_1$, then it converges (uniformly) for $s_1 \leq s < \infty$. HINT: Use Theorem 4d of Chapter 4. Deduce that for each series there is a number γ_c, the *abscissa of convergence*, such that the series (6) converges for $s > \gamma_c$ and diverges for $s < \gamma_c$.

It follows from Problem 1 that if

$$D = \left\{ s \, \middle| \, \sum_{n=1}^{\infty} b_n e^{-\lambda_n s} \text{ converges} \right\},$$

then D consists of the set $\gamma_c < s < \infty$ together with, in some cases, the point $s = \gamma_c$. It is evident that if $\phi(s)$ is the sum of the series (6) for $s \in D$, then $\phi(s)$ is continuous in D.

Every generalized Dirichlet series thus has an abscissa of absolute convergence γ_a and an abscissa of convergence γ_c. Clearly $-\infty \leq \gamma_c \leq \gamma_a \leq \infty$.

2. Show that for classical Dirichlet series ($\lambda_n = \log n$) the relation $\gamma_c \leq \gamma_a \leq \gamma_c + 1$ is always valid. HINT: See Problem 2 of Sec. 1. Give an example of a classical Dirichlet series for which $\gamma_a = \gamma_c$; one for which $\gamma_a = \gamma_c + 1$.

3. With the notation of Problem 1 show that the series

$$(7) \qquad \sum_{n=1}^{\infty} - b_n \lambda_n e^{-\lambda_n s} ,$$

obtained by formal term by term differentiation of $\sum_{n=1}^{\infty} b_n e^{-\lambda_s s}$, has the same abscissa of absolute convergence and the same abscissa of convergence as the series (6). HINT: For any $\epsilon > 0$ there is a number $\lambda(\epsilon)$ such that $\lambda e^{-\epsilon \lambda}$ is a decreasing function of λ for $\lambda \geq \lambda(\epsilon)$. Prove that the sum of the series (6), $\phi(s)$, is differentiable for $s > \gamma_c$ and that for $s > \gamma_c$, $\phi'(s)$ is the sum of the series (7).

4. Real Analytic Functions

By a *neighborhood* of a point x_0 on the real axis is meant a set of the form $\{x \mid |x - x_0| < \rho\}$ where $\rho > 0$.

DEFINITION 4a. A function $f(x)$ defined on the interval[1] $I = \{a < x < b\}$ is said to be a (real) analytic function if it is infinitely differentiable for $x \in I$ and

[1] a may be finite or $-\infty$, and b finite or $+\infty$.

if for each point $x_0 \in I$, $f(x)$ is in some neighborhood of x_0 the sum of its Taylor series with center x_0.

Note that the domain of definition of a real analytic function is always an interval (finite or infinite) without end points. Almost all the familiar functions of elementary analysis are analytic functions when restricted to any interval not containing an obvious singularity. The functions in Table 6 are analytic in the indicated intervals, as can be seen using the results (and methods) of Chapter 2.

Table 6

Function	a	b
$p(x)$ (polynomial)	$-\infty$	∞
e^x	$-\infty$	∞
$\sin x$	$-\infty$	∞
$\cos x$	$-\infty$	∞
$\log x$	0	∞
$\sqrt{1 + x}$	-1	∞
$\sqrt{1 - x^2}$	-1	1

Let us denote by $\mathfrak{A}[I]$ the class of all real analytic functions defined for $x \in I$, where $I = \{a < x < b\}$.

The following simple theorems show that the class $\mathfrak{A}[I]$ is closed under various simple operations.

THEOREM 4b. If $f(x) \in \mathfrak{A}[I]$, then

1. $f'(x) \in \mathfrak{A}[I]$;
2. $\int_c^x f(t) \, dt \in \mathfrak{A}[I]$ for any $c \in I$.

Proof. Choose $x_0 \in I$. By Theorem 2d of Chapter 2 if[1]

$$(1) \qquad \sum_{n=0}^{\infty} a_n(x - x_0)^n \qquad a_n = \frac{1}{n!} \left(\frac{d}{dx}\right)^n f(x) \Big|_{x=x_0}$$

is the Taylor series for $f(x)$ with center x_0, the Taylor series for $f'(x)$ with this center is

$$(2) \qquad \sum_{n=0}^{\infty} na_n(x - x_0)^{n-1}.$$

[1] The result referred to is stated for Maclaurin series, but its extension to Taylor series is obvious.

By assumption the series **(1)** converges to $f(x)$ for $|x - x_0| < \rho$ for some $\rho > 0$. By Theorem 2a of the present chapter the series **(2)** converges to $f'(x)$ for $|x - x_0| < \rho$. This proves Conclusion 1. Conclusion 2 is similar.

THEOREM 4c. If $f_1(x)$, $f_2(x) \in \mathfrak{A}[I]$, then

1. $\alpha_1 f_1(x) + \alpha_2 f_2(x) \in \mathfrak{A}[I]$ for any real numbers α_1 and α_2;
2. $f_1(x)f_2(x) \in \mathfrak{A}[I]$.

Proof. Left as an exercise.

THEOREM 4d. If $f(x) \in \mathfrak{A}[I]$ and if $f(x) \neq 0$ for $x \in I$, then $1/f(x) \in \mathfrak{A}[I]$.

Proof. Left as an exercise.

EXAMPLE 1. Show that $\tan x \in \mathfrak{A}[-\pi/2, \pi/2]$. Since $\cos x \in \mathfrak{A}[-\infty, \infty]$, a fortiori $\cos x \in \mathfrak{A}[-\pi/2, \pi/2]$, and since $\cos x \neq 0$ for $|x| < \pi/2$, $1/\cos x \in \mathfrak{A}[-\pi/2, \pi/2]$ by Theorem 4d. Again $\sin x \in \mathfrak{A}[-\pi/2, \pi/2]$. We now apply Conclusion 2 of Theorem 4c to show that $\tan x = \sin x(1/\cos x) \in \mathfrak{A}[-\pi/2, \pi/2]$, as desired.

Let $f(x)$ be an infinitely differentiable function for $a < x < b$. If at a point $c \in I$, we have

$$f^{(k)}(c) = 0 \qquad (k = 0, 1, \cdots, \; n-1),$$
$$f^{(n)}(c) \neq 0,$$

then c is said to be a zero of order n for $f(x)$. If

$$f^{(k)}(c) = 0 \qquad (k = 0, 1, \cdots),$$

then c is said to be a zero of infinite order for $f(x)$. It is evident that none of the analytic functions of our table (except the identically zero function) has a zero of infinite order. The following result shows that this is true generally.

LEMMA 4e. Let $f(x) \in \mathfrak{A}[a, b]$. If $c \; (a < c < b)$ is a zero of infinite order for $f(x)$, then $f(x) \equiv 0$ for $a < x < b$.

Proof. Since $f(x) \in \mathfrak{A}[a, b]$, there is for each point $x_0 \, (a < x_0 < b)$ a positive number ρ such that the Taylor series for $f(x)$ with center x_0 converges to $f(x)$ for $|x - x_0| < \rho$. Since ρ depends upon x_0, we shall write $\rho(x_0)$ in place of ρ. We note that if x_0 is a zero of infinite order for $f(x)$, then $f(x) = 0$ for $|x - x_0| < \rho(x_0)$. This is because all the coefficients of the Taylor series with center x_0 vanish. Let us set

$$b_1 = \text{l.u.b. } \{t \mid f(x) = 0 \text{ for } c \leq x < t\},$$
$$a_1 = \text{g.l.b. } \{t \mid f(x) = 0 \text{ for } t < x \leq c\},$$

Then $f(x) = 0$ for $a_1 < x < b_1$. [Since $f(x) = 0$ for $|x - c| < \rho(c)$, it is evident that $a_1 < b_1$.] We assert that $b_1 = b$ and $a_1 = a$. Suppose to the contrary that $b_1 < b$. Since $f(x) = 0$ for $a_1 < x < b_1$, it follows that for any noninteger k, $f^{(k)}(x) = 0$ for $a_1 < x < b_1$. Since by assumption $f^{(k)}(x)$ is continuous, we have $f^{(k)}(b_1) = 0$. This is true for each k; consequently b_1 is a zero of infinite order for $f(x)$. It now follows that $f(x) = 0$ for $|x - b_1| < \rho(b_1)$. This evidently contradicts the definition of b_1. Thus $b_1 = b$, and similarly $a_1 = a$.

THEOREM 4f. Let I_0 be a subinterval of the open interval I. If $f_1(x), f_2(x) \in \mathfrak{A}[I]$ and if $f_1(x) = f_2(x)$ for $x \in I_0$, then $f_1(x) = f_2(x)$ for $x \in I$.

Proof. By Theorem 4c, $f_1(x) - f_2(x) \in \mathfrak{A}[I]$. Since this function is 0 for $x \in I_0$, any interior point c of I_0 is a zero of infinite order for $f_1(x) - f_2(x)$. Apply Lemma 4e.

An equivalent statement is that the behavior of an analytic function throughout its interval of definition is determined by its behavior on any subinterval, however small. This remarkable fact is one of the most important properties of analytic functions.

The following result asserts that the sum of a power series is necessarily an analytic function.

THEOREM 4g. Let the power series

$$(3) \qquad \qquad \sum_{n=0}^{\infty} a_n(x - c)^n$$

have radius of convergence $r > 0$, and let $A(x)$ be the sum of the series (3) for $|x - c| < r$. Then

$$A(x) \in \mathfrak{A}[c - r, c + r].$$

Proof. Take any x_0 $(c - r < x_0 < c + r)$. We must show that the Taylor series for $A(x)$ with center x_0

$$(4) \qquad \qquad \sum_{m=0}^{\infty} \frac{1}{m!} A^{(m)}(x_0) (x - x_0)^m$$

converges to $A(x)$ for $|x - x_0| < \rho(x_0)$ for some positive $\rho(x_0)$.

Since
$$\left(\frac{d}{dx}\right)^m x^n = x^{n-m} n(n-1) \cdots (n - m + 1),$$

it follows, using Theorem 2b, that

$$\frac{1}{m!} A^{(m)}(x_0) = \sum_{n=0}^{\infty} a_n \binom{n}{m} (x_0 - c)^{n-m} \qquad (m = 0, 1, \cdots).$$

Thus

$$\sum_{m=0}^{\infty} \frac{1}{m!} A^{(m)}(x_0) (x - x_0)^m = \sum_{m=0}^{\infty} (x - x_0)^m \sum_{n=0}^{\infty} a_n \binom{n}{m} (x_0 - c)^{n-m}$$

Fubini's theorem, see Sec. 4 Chapter 5, asserts that

$$\sum_{m=0}^{\infty} (x - x_0)^m \sum_{n=0}^{\infty} a_n \binom{n}{m} (x_0 - c)^n = \sum_{n=0}^{\infty} a_n \sum_{m=0}^{\infty} \binom{n}{m} (x - x_0)^m (x_0 - c)^{n-m}$$

$$= \sum_{n=0}^{\infty} a_n (x - c)^n = A(x)$$

for all x, for which

$$\sum_{n=0}^{\infty} |a_n| \sum_{m=0}^{\infty} \binom{n}{m} |x - x_0|^m |x_0 - c|^{n-m} < \infty .$$

Now

$$\sum_{m=0}^{\infty} \binom{n}{m} |x - x_0|^m |x_0 - c|^{n-m} = \{|x - x_0| + |x_0 - c|\}^n ,$$

and by Theorem 2a the series

$$\sum_{n=0}^{\infty} |a_n| \{|x - x_0| + |x_0 - c|\}^n$$

is convergent if $|x - x_0| + |x_0 - c| < r$. Thus the series (4) converges to $A(x)$ for $|x - x_0| < \rho(x_0)$ if $\rho(x_0) = r - |x_0 - c|$.

PROBLEMS

1. (a) Let I_0 be an open subinterval of the interval I. Show that if $f \in \mathfrak{A} [I]$ and if f_0 is the restriction of $f(x)$ to I_0, then $f_0 \in \mathfrak{A} [I_0]$.

(b) Let I_1 and I_2 be two open intervals such that $I_1 \cap I_2 \neq \varnothing$. Suppose that $f_1 \in \mathfrak{A} [I_1]$, $f_2 \in \mathfrak{A} [I_2]$ and that $f_1(x) = f_2(x)$ for $x \in I_1 \cap I_2$. Show that if $f(x)$ is defined as $f_1(x)$ for $x \in I_1$ and $f_2(x)$ for $x \in I_2$, then $f(x) \in \mathfrak{A} [I_1 \cup I_2]$.

2. Prove Theorem 4c.

3. Prove Theorem 4d.

4. Show in detail that if $f(x)$ is defined as e^{-1/x^2} for $x \neq 0$ and as 0 for $x = 0$, then $f(x)$ is infinitely differentiable for $-\infty < x < \infty$ and that $c = 0$ is a zero of infinite order for $f(x)$. Does $f(x) \in \mathfrak{A} [-\infty, \infty]$? Explain.

5. Using Theorems 4f and 4g, prove that if $f \in \mathfrak{A}\,[I]$ and if the Taylor series for $f(x)$ with center $x_0 \in I$,

$$(5) \qquad\qquad \sum_{n=0}^{\infty} \frac{f^{(n)}(x_0)}{n!}\,(x - x_0)^n \,,$$

has radius of convergence $r(x_0)$, then the series **(5)** converges to $f(x)$ for all $x \in I \cap \{|\,x - x_0\,| < r(x_0)\}$.

Note that Definition 4a says only that the series **(5)** converges to $f(x)$ for x in *some* neighborhood of x_0.

[7]

Additional Topics in Fourier Series

1. (C,1) Summability

Given an infinite series $\sum_0^\infty c_k$, let $s_n = \sum_{k=0}^n c_k$ be the partial sum of index n. We set

$$\sigma_N = \frac{1}{N+1} \sum_{n=0}^N s_n = \sum_{k=0}^N \left(1 - \frac{k}{N+1}\right) c_k$$

so that σ_N is the average of s_0, s_1, \cdots, s_N. We say that the series $\sum_0^\infty c_k$ is summable $(C,1)$ to the value $\lim\limits_{N\to\infty} \sigma_N$ whenever this limit exists, and we write

$$(C,1) \sum_{k=0}^\infty c_k = \lim_{N\to\infty} \sigma_N .$$

In Sec. 6 of Chapter 5 it was shown that if $\lim\limits_{n\to\infty} s_n = s$, then $\lim\limits_{N\to\infty} \sigma_N = s$ too; that is, $\sum_{k=0}^\infty c_k = s$ implies that $(C,1) \sum_{k=0}^\infty c_k = s$. Simple examples show that $(C,1) \sum_{k=0}^\infty c_k$ may exist even though $\sum_{k=0}^\infty c_k$ does not.

We proved in Chapter 3 that if $f \in \mathfrak{F}$ and if

(1) $$f \sim \tfrac{1}{2}a_0 + \sum_{k=1}^\infty (a_k \cos kx + b_k \sin kx),$$

then the series **(1)** converges to $f(x_0)$ if f is differentiable at x_0. In the present section we shall prove that the series **(1)** is $(C,1)$ summable to $f(x_0)$ if f is continuous at x_0.

The Dirichlet kernel $D_N(x)$ of index N is defined by the formula

$$D_N(x) = \tfrac{1}{2} + \sum_{n=1}^N \cos nx.$$

By Lemma 4a of Chapter 3 we have

$$D_N(x) = \frac{\sin (N + \tfrac{1}{2}) x}{2 \sin (x/2)} .$$

149

Let us define

(2) $K_N(x) = (N + 1)^{-1} [D_0(x) + D_1(x) + \cdots + D_N(x)]$

$$= \tfrac{1}{2} + \sum_{n=0}^{N} \cos nx \left(1 - \frac{n}{N + 1}\right).$$

$K_N(x)$ is called the Fejer kernel of index N. By definition the $(C,1)$ sum of the series **(1)** at $x = x_0$ is $\lim_{N \to \infty} \sigma_N(x_0)$ where

(3) $\sigma_N(x) = \dfrac{a_0}{2} + \sum_{n=1}^{N} (a_n \cos nx + b_n \sin nx) \left(1 - \dfrac{n}{N + 1}\right)$

or alternatively

$$\sigma_N(x) = (N + 1)^{-1} [s_0(x) + s_1(x) + \cdots + s_n(x)]$$

where $s_n(x) = \dfrac{a_0}{2} + \sum_{k=1}^{n} (a_k \cos kx + b_k \sin kx)$

is the partial sum of index n of the series **(1)**.

LEMMA 1a. With the above definitions

$$\sigma_N(x) - f(x) = \frac{1}{\pi} \int_{-\pi}^{\pi} [f(x - t) - f(x)] K_N(t) \, dt .$$

Proof. By Theorem 4a of Chapter 3

$$s_n(x) - f(x) = \frac{1}{\pi} \int_{-\pi}^{\pi} [f(x - t) - f(x)] D_n(t) \, dt .$$

Summing this equality over $n = 0, 1, \cdots, N$ and dividing by $N + 1$, we obtain the desired result.

LEMMA 1b.

$$K_N(x) = \frac{1}{2(N + 1)} \cdot \frac{\sin^2 [(N + 1)/2]x}{\sin^2 (x/2)} .$$

Proof. By **(2)**

$$K_N(x) = \left[(N + 1) \, 2 \sin \frac{x}{2}\right]^{-1} \left[\sin \frac{x}{2} + \sin \frac{3x}{2} + \cdots + \sin \frac{2N + 1}{2} x\right] .$$

Now use the result of Problem 2 of Sec. 4, Chapter 3.

We note that as a consequence of the above, we have

(4) $K_N(x) \geq 0$ $(N = 0, 1, \cdots, -\infty < x < \infty),$

and thus since

$$\frac{1}{\pi} \int_{-\pi}^{\pi} K_N(x)\, dx = \frac{1}{N+1} \sum_{n=0}^{N} \int_{-\pi}^{\pi} D_n(x)\, dx = 1 \,,$$

it follows that

(5)
$$\frac{1}{\pi} \int_{-\pi}^{\pi} |K_N(x)|\, dx = 1.$$

THEOREM 1c. If for $f \in \mathfrak{F}$

1. $f \sim \dfrac{a_0}{2} + \displaystyle\sum_{n=1}^{\infty} a_n \cos nx + b_n \sin nx,$

2. $\sigma_N(x) = \dfrac{a_0}{2} + \displaystyle\sum_{n=1}^{N} (a_n \cos nx + b_n \sin nx)\left(1 - \dfrac{n}{N+1}\right).$

3. f is continuous at x_0,

then
$$\lim_{N \to \infty} \sigma_N(x_0) = f(x_0).$$

Proof. Given $\epsilon > 0$, there is, by Assumption 3, a $\delta > 0$ such that

(6)
$$|f(x_0 - t) - f(x_0)| < \epsilon \qquad \text{if } |t| < \delta.$$

Next let

(7)
$$M = \text{l.u.b. } |f(x)| \qquad (-\pi \le x \le \pi).$$

M is finite because of Theorem 2c of the Appendix. Since $f(x)$ periodic with period 2π, (7) actually holds for $-\infty < x < \infty$. We have

$$\sigma_N(x_0) - f(x_0) = I_1 + I_2 + I_3$$

where
$$I_1 = \frac{1}{\pi} \int_{-\delta}^{\delta} [f(x_0 - t) - f(x_0)]\, K_N(t)\, dt,$$

$$I_2 = \frac{1}{\pi} \int_{\delta}^{\pi} [f(x_0 - t) - f(x_0)]\, K_N(t)\, dt,$$

$$I_3 = \frac{1}{\pi} \int_{-\pi}^{-\delta} [f(x_0 - t) - f(x_0)]\, K_N(t)\, dt.$$

Using (6), Lemmas 3b and 3c of Chapter 2, and (5), we see that

$$|I_1| \le \frac{1}{\pi} \int_{-\delta}^{\delta} \epsilon\, |K_N(t)|\, dt \le \epsilon \frac{1}{\pi} \int_{-\pi}^{\pi} K_N(t)\, dt = \epsilon.$$

Again, since by (7)

$$|f(x_0 - t) - f(x_0)| \le |f(x_0 - t)| + |f(x_0)| \le 2M ,$$

we find that

$$|I_2| \le \frac{1}{\pi} \int_\delta^\pi 2M \, K_N(t) \, dt$$

and since

$$K_N(t) \le \frac{1}{2(N+1)} \frac{1}{\sin^2 (t/2)} ,$$

$$|I_2| \le \frac{M}{\pi(N+1)} \int_\delta^\pi \sin^{-2} \left(\frac{t}{2}\right) dt.$$

Similarly

$$|I_3| \le \frac{M}{\pi(N+1)} \int_{-\pi}^{-\delta} \sin^{-2} \left(\frac{t}{2}\right) dt.$$

If N_0 is so chosen that

$$\frac{M}{\pi(N_0+1)} \int_\delta^\pi \sin^{-2} \left(\frac{t}{2}\right) dt < \epsilon ,$$

then if $N \ge N_0$,

$$|I_2| < \epsilon, \qquad |I_3| < \epsilon ,$$

so that for $N \ge N_0$ we have

$$|\sigma_N(x_0) - f(x_0)| < 3\epsilon ,$$

and our proof is complete.

An interesting property of the $(C,1)$ sums $\sigma_N(x)$ is that if the graph of $f(x)$ lies in a horizontal band, the graph of $\sigma_N(x)$ is confined to the same band.

THEOREM 1d. If

1. $f \in \mathfrak{F}$,
2. σ_N is defined by (3),
3. $a \le f(x) \le A$ (all x),

then

$$a \le \sigma_N(x) \le A \qquad (\text{all } x, N = 0, 1, \cdots).$$

Proof. We have, arguing as in Lemma 1a,

$$\sigma_N(x) - a = \frac{1}{\pi} \int_{-\pi}^\pi [f(x - t) - a] \, K_N(t) \, dt .$$

Since $f(x - t) - a \ge 0$ and since by (4) $K_N(t) \ge 0$, it follows that $\sigma_N(x) - a \ge 0$, etc.

PROBLEMS

1. Prove that if $f \in \mathfrak{F}$, the Fourier series of f (with $x = x_0$) is $(C,1)$ summable to $\frac{1}{2}[f(x_0 +) + f(x_0 -)]$ at all points x_0.

2. Uniform Continuity

DEFINITION 2a. Let $f(x)$ be defined on a subset $S \subset \Re$. Then $f(x)$ is said to be uniformly continuous on S if given $\epsilon > 0$, there is a $\delta > 0$ such that

(1) $$|f(x_1) - f(x)| < \epsilon$$

if $x_1, x \in S$ and if $|x_1 - x| < \delta$.

Note that if $f(x)$ is continuous at each point of S, then given ϵ *and given* $x_1 \in S$ there is a $\delta > 0$ such that $|f(x_1) - f(x)| < \epsilon$ if $x \in R$ and if $|x_1 - x| < \delta$. However, in general δ will depend on x_1, and it will not be possible to chose a single δ such that **(1)** holds for all $x_1 \in S$. If for each $\epsilon > 0$ this is possible, $f(x)$ is uniformly continuous.

The following result which is fundamental is proved as Theorem 2e of the Appendix.

"If $f(x)$ is continuous at each point of the finite closed interval $a \le x \le b$, it is uniformly continuous there." (An interval is closed if it contains both of its end points.)

Let us write $f \in \mathfrak{F} \cap \mathfrak{C}$ if $f \in \mathfrak{F}$ and if f is continuous on $-\infty < x < \infty$.

THEOREM 2b. If $f \in \mathfrak{F} \cap \mathfrak{C}$ and if $\sigma_N(x)$ is defined as in **(4)** of Sec. 1, then

$$\lim_{N \to \infty} \sigma_N(x) = f(x)$$

uniformly for $-\pi \le x \le \pi$.

Proof. By the above the function $f(x)$ is uniformly continuous in the interval $I = \{-2\pi \le x \le 2\pi\}$. Therefore given any $\epsilon > 0$, there is a $\delta > 0$ such that

$$|f(x - t) - f(x)| < \epsilon \qquad \text{if } |t| < \delta$$

and if $x - t$ and x lie in I. We may clearly assume $\delta \le \pi$; then we have $|f(x - t) - f(x)| < \epsilon$ for $-\pi \le x \le \pi$, $|t| < \delta$. Let $M = \text{l.u.b.} \; |f(x)|$ $(-\infty < x < \infty)$. If N_0 is so chosen that $M [\pi(N_0 + 1)]^{-1} \int_\delta^\pi [\sin (t/2)]^{-2} dt < \epsilon$, then referring to the proof of Theorem 1c, we see that for $-\pi \le x \le \pi$

$$|f(x) - \sigma_N(x)| < 3\epsilon \qquad \text{if } N \ge N_0, \qquad \text{Q.E.D.}$$

The following result the demonstration of which is essentially the same as that of Theorem 2b is needed in Sec. 3.

COROLLARY 2c. Let $f \in \mathfrak{F}$, and let f be continuous for $a \le x \le b$; then

$$\lim_{N \to \infty} \sigma_N(x) = f(x)$$

uniformly for $a \le x \le b$.

Using Theorem 2b, we can give an easy proof of the following fundamental result known as the "Weierstrass approximation theorem."

THEOREM 2d. If $f(x)$ is a continuous function for $a \leq x \leq b$, then given $\epsilon > 0$ there is a polynomial $p(x) = p_0 + p_1 x + \cdots + p_m x^m$ such that

$$|f(x) - p(x)| < \epsilon \qquad \text{for } a \leq x \leq b.$$

Equivalently, a continuous function on a finite closed interval can be uniformly approximated there by polynomials.

Proof. We may suppose without loss of generality that $-\pi < a < b < \pi$. Extend $f(x)$ to the interval $-\pi \leq x \leq \pi$ so that it is continuous there and so that $f(-\pi) = f(\pi)$; then extend $f(x)$ to the entire real axis by periodicity, $f(x + 2\pi) = f(x)$. The extended function, which we continue to denote by $f(x)$, belongs to $\mathfrak{F} \cap \mathfrak{C}$. By Theorem 2b if

$$f(x) \sim \frac{a_0}{2} + \sum_1^\infty a_n \cos nx + b_n \sin nx ,$$

then for N sufficiently large we shall have

$$|f(x) - \sigma_N(x)| < \frac{\epsilon}{2} \qquad (-\infty < x < \infty)$$

where $\qquad \sigma_N(x) = \dfrac{a_0}{2} + \displaystyle\sum_{n=1}^N (a_n \cos nx + b_n \sin nx) \left(1 - \dfrac{n}{N+1}\right).$

Let

$$\sum_{k=0}^\infty \frac{\sigma_N^{(k)}(0)}{k!} x^k$$

be the Maclaurin expansion for $\sigma_N(x)$. Since $\sigma_N(x)$ is a finite linear combination of sines and cosines, it is easy to see that there exists an integer m such that

$$\left| \sigma_N(x) - \sum_{k=0}^m \frac{\sigma_N^{(k)}(0)}{k!} x^k \right| < \frac{\epsilon}{2} \qquad (-\pi \leq x \leq \pi).$$

Clearly

$$p(x) = \sum_{k=0}^m \frac{\sigma_N^{(k)}(0)}{k!} x^k$$

has the desired property.

PROBLEMS

1. Prove that for $N = 0, 1, 2, \cdots$,

$$K_N(x) \leq \begin{cases} \dfrac{\pi^2}{2} \cdot \dfrac{1}{(N+1) x^2} \\[2ex] \dfrac{\pi^2}{8} \cdot (N+1) \end{cases} \qquad (|x| \leq \pi).$$

HINT: $\sin x \geq 2x/\pi$ for $0 \leq x \leq \pi/2$. This is easily seen by drawing graphs of $y = \sin x$ and $y = 2x/\pi$.

A function $f(x)$ defined on an interval I is said to belong to the class Lip $\alpha[I]$ $(0 < \alpha \leq 1)$ if there is a constant A, depending on f, such that

(2) $$|f(x_1) - f(x_2)| \leq A \, |x_1 - x_2|^\alpha \qquad (x_1, x_2 \in I).$$

Let \mathfrak{F}_α be the class of these functions $f(x)$ defined for $-\infty < x < \infty$ and satisfying:

1. $f(x)$ is periodic with period 2π there;
2. $f(x)$ belongs to the class Lip $\alpha[-\infty < x < \infty]$.

2. Prove that if $f \in \mathfrak{F}_\alpha$, then

$$|\sigma_N(x) - f(x)| \leq B_\alpha A(N+1)^{-\alpha} \qquad (N = 0, 1, \cdots)$$

where B_α is a constant depending only on α and where A is the constant in (2). HINT:

$$\sigma_N(x) - f(x) = I_1 + I_2 + I_3$$

where
$$I_1 = \frac{1}{\pi} \int_{-(N+1)^{-1}}^{(N+1)^{-1}} [f(x-t) - f(x)] \, K_N(t) \, dt \, .$$

$$I_2 = \frac{1}{\pi} \int_{(N+1)^{-1}}^{\pi} [f(x-t) - f(x)] \, K_N(t) \, dt \, ,$$

$$I_3 = \frac{1}{\pi} \int_{-\pi}^{-(N+1)^{-1}} [f(x-t) - f(x)] \, K_N(t) \, dt \, .$$

3. Parseval's Equality

In this section we shall prove Parseval's equality, a brief statement of which was given in Sec. 3 of Chapter 3.

THEOREM 3a. If

1. $f \in \mathfrak{F}$,

2. $f \sim \dfrac{a_0}{2} + \displaystyle\sum_{n=1}^{\infty} a_n \cos nx + b_n \sin nx,$

then

(1) $$\tfrac{1}{2}a_0^2 + \sum_{n=1}^{\infty} (a_n^2 + b_n^2) = \frac{1}{\pi} \int_{-\pi}^{\pi} f(x)^2 \, dx \, .$$

Proof. By Bessel's inequality, Theorem 3a of Chapter 3,

$$\tfrac{1}{2}a_0^2 + \sum_{n=1}^{\infty} (a_n^2 + b_n^2) \leq \frac{1}{\pi} \int_{-\pi}^{\pi} f(x)^2 \, dx.$$

Before giving our proof for $f \in \mathfrak{F}$, let us, for the purposes of illustration, consider the simpler case $f \in \mathfrak{F} \cap \mathfrak{C}$. For $f \in \mathfrak{F} \cap \mathfrak{C}$ $\sigma_N(x)$ converges uniformly to $f(x)$ as $N \to \infty$ on $-\pi \leq x \leq \pi$ by Theorem 2b. Consequently $\sigma_N(x)^2$ converges uniformly to $f(x)^2$ as $N \to \infty$ on $-\pi \leq x \leq \pi$ (see Theorem 3a of Chapter 4). By Theorem 2b of Chapter 4

$$\lim_{N \to \infty} \frac{1}{\pi} \int_{-\pi}^{\pi} \sigma_N(x)^2 \, dx = \frac{1}{\pi} \int_{-\pi}^{\pi} f(x)^2 \, dx.$$

Thus given $\epsilon > 0$, there is an integer N such that

$$\frac{1}{\pi} \int_{-\pi}^{\pi} \sigma_N(x)^2 \, dx \geq \frac{1}{\pi} \int_{-\pi}^{\pi} f(x)^2 \, dx - \epsilon.$$

An evident computation gives

$$\frac{1}{\pi} \int_{-\pi}^{\pi} \sigma_N(x)^2 \, dx = \tfrac{1}{2}a_0^2 + \sum_{n=1}^{N} (a_n^2 + b_n^2) \left(1 - \frac{n}{N+1}\right)^2.$$

Combining these results, we find that

$$\tfrac{1}{2}a_0^2 + \sum_{n=1}^{\infty} (a_n^2 + b_n^2) \geq \tfrac{1}{2}a_0^2 + \sum_{n=1}^{N} (a_n^2 + b_n^2) \left(1 - \frac{n}{N+1}\right)^2 \geq \frac{1}{\pi} \int_{-\pi}^{\pi} f(x)^2 \, dx - \epsilon,$$

or since ϵ is arbitrary,

$$(2) \qquad \tfrac{1}{2}a_0^2 + \sum_{n=1}^{\infty} (a_n^2 + b_n^2) \geq \frac{1}{\pi} \int_{-\pi}^{\pi} f(x)^2 \, dx.$$

The inequalities (1) and (2) taken together give us our desired result.

If $f \in \mathfrak{F}$, the proof is the same except that Corollary 2c, and Theorem 3c of Chapter 4 are used in place of Theorem 2b and Theorem 2b of Chapter 4.

THEOREM 3b. If

1. $f \in \mathfrak{F}$, $g \in \mathfrak{F}$,

2. $f \sim \tfrac{1}{2}a_0 + \sum_{n=1}^{\infty} a_n \cos nx + b_n \sin nx$,

3. $g \sim \tfrac{1}{2}c_0 + \sum_{n=1}^{\infty} c_n \cos nx + d_n \sin nx$,

then

(3) $\frac{1}{2}a_0 c_0 + \sum_{n=1}^{\infty} (a_n c_n + b_n d_n) = \frac{1}{\pi} \int_{-\pi}^{\pi} f(x) g(x) dx$.

Proof. $f(x) \pm g(x) \in \mathfrak{F}$, and

$f(x) \pm g(x) \sim \frac{1}{2}(a_0 \pm c_0) + \sum_{n=1}^{\infty} (a_n \pm c_n) \cos nx + (b_n \pm d_n) \sin nx$.

By Theorem 3a

(4) $\frac{1}{2}(a_0 \pm c_0)^2 + \sum_{n=1}^{\infty} (a_n \pm c_n)^2 + (b_n \pm d_n)^2 = \frac{1}{\pi} \int_{-\pi}^{\pi} [f(x) \pm g(x)]^2 dx.$

If we subtract (4) with \pm taken as $-$ from (4) with \pm taken as $+$ and employ
the identity
$$(A + B)^2 - (A - B)^2 = 4AB$$

we shall obtain four times (3).

In the following section we shall need the complex form of Parseval's
equality. We recall that for $f \in \mathfrak{F}^c$ if

$$c_n = \frac{1}{2\pi} \int_{-\pi}^{\pi} f(x) e(-nx) dx ,$$

then $f(x) \sim \sum_{-\infty}^{\infty} c_n e(nx)$.

THEOREM 3c. If

 1. $f \in \mathfrak{F}^c$,

 2. $f \sim \sum_{-\infty}^{\infty} c_n e(nx)$,

then $\sum_{-\infty}^{\infty} |c_n|^2 = \frac{1}{2\pi} \int_{-\pi}^{\pi} |f(x)|^2 dx.$

Proof. Left as an exercise.

THEOREM 3d. If

 1. $f \in \mathfrak{F}^c, g \in \mathfrak{F}^c$,

 2. $f \sim \sum_{-\infty}^{\infty} c_n e(nx)$,

 3. $g \sim \sum_{-\infty}^{\infty} d_n e(nx)$,

then

$$\sum_{-\infty}^{\infty} c_n \, d_n^* = \frac{1}{2\pi} \int_{-\pi}^{\pi} f(x) \, g(x)^* \, dx.$$

Proof. Left as an exercise.

EXAMPLE 1. If we combine Theorem 3c with Problem 12 of Sec. 2 of Chapter 4, we obtain the striking identity

$$\sum_{-\infty}^{\infty} J_n(x)^2 = 1 \qquad (-\infty < x < \infty).$$

PROBLEMS

1. Use the ideas employed in the proof of Theorem 7d of Chapter 3 to deduce Theorem 3c from Theorem 3a.

2. Deduce Theorem 3d from Theorem 3c.

4. Convolution

Throughout this section we use Fourier series in their complex form. For $h, g \in \mathfrak{F}^c$, let us define a new function $h \star g$ by means of the formula

(1) $$h \star g \cdot (x) = \frac{1}{2\pi} \int_{-\pi}^{\pi} h(x - t) \, g(t) \, dt.$$

For x fixed, $h(x - t)$ and $g(t)$ are piecewise continuous functions of t, and the product $h(x - t) \, g(t)$ is therefore also a piecewise continuous function of t. Thus the integral **(1)** is well defined for all x $(-\infty < x < \infty)$. Furthermore

$$h \star g \cdot (x + 2\pi) = \frac{1}{2\pi} \int_{-\pi}^{\pi} h(x + 2\pi - t) \, g(t) \, dt$$

$$= \frac{1}{2\pi} \int_{-\pi}^{\pi} h(x - t) \, g(t) \, dt$$

$$= h \star g \cdot (x);$$

that is, $h \star g$ is periodic with period 2π. If $h \star g$ were piecewise continuous, it would thus belong to \mathfrak{F}^c. Actually $h \star g$ is continuous. *Assuming* this for the moment, let us compute the nth complex Fourier coefficient c_n of $h \star g$; we have

$$c_n = \frac{1}{2\pi} \int_{-\pi}^{\pi} h \star g \cdot (x) \, e(-nx) \, dx$$

(2) $$= \frac{1}{2\pi} \int_{-\pi}^{\pi} e(-nx) \, dx \, \frac{1}{2\pi} \int_{-\pi}^{\pi} h(x - t) \, g(t) \, dt.$$

Let us *assume* that it is possible to invert the order of integrations in this double integral; we then have

$$c_n = \frac{1}{2\pi} \int_{-\pi}^{\pi} g(t) \, dt \, \frac{1}{2\pi} \int_{-\pi}^{\pi} h(x - t) \, e(- nx) \, dx \, .$$

Now $e(- nx) = e(- n\{x - t\}) \, e(- nt)$ (see Sec. 7 of Chapter 3). Thus

$$c_n = \frac{1}{2\pi} \int_{-\pi}^{\pi} g(t) \, e(- nt) \, dt \, \frac{1}{2\pi} \int_{-\pi}^{\pi} h(x - t) \, e(- n\{x - t\}) \, dx$$

$$= \frac{1}{2\pi} \int_{-\pi}^{\pi} g(t) \, e(- nt) \, dt \, \frac{1}{2\pi} \int_{-\pi-t}^{\pi-t} h(u) \, e(- nu) \, du.$$

In this last step we have made the change of variables $x - t = u$ in the x integral. Let us set

(3) $\qquad a_n = \frac{1}{2\pi} \int_{-\pi}^{\pi} g(x) \, e(- nx), \qquad b_n = \frac{1}{2\pi} \int_{-\pi}^{\pi} h(x) \, e(- nx) \, dx$

so that

(4) $\qquad\qquad g(x) \sim \sum_{-\infty}^{\infty} a_n \, e(nx), \qquad h(x) \sim \sum_{-\infty}^{\infty} b_n \, e(nx).$

By Problem 4 of Sec. 1 of Chapter 3

$$\frac{1}{2\pi} \int_{-\pi-t}^{\pi-t} h(u) \, e(- nu) \, du = \frac{1}{2\pi} \int_{-\pi}^{\pi} h(u) \, e(- nu) \, du$$

$$= b_n.$$

Thus

(5) $\qquad\qquad c_n = b_n \cdot \frac{1}{2\pi} \int_{-\pi}^{\pi} g(t) \, e(- nt) \, dt = b_n \, a_n,$

or equivalently

(6) $\qquad\qquad h \star g \cdot (x) \sim \sum_{-\infty}^{\infty} b_n \, a_n \, e(nx).$

This elegant formula is of the greatest importance, and our objective in the present section is to prove it. The informal proof given above is not satisfactory since:

1. it was assumed that $h \star g \cdot (x)$ is continuous;

2. it was assumed that the order of the integrations in the iterated integral (2), the integrand of which may possess severe discontinuities, can be inverted.

It is possible to prove both of these statements and thus to turn our informal proof into a correct one. However it is simpler to base a proof of (**5**) and (**6**) on Parseval's equality, and this is what we shall do.

LEMMA 4a. If $h(t) \in \mathfrak{F}^c$ and if

$$h(t) \sim \sum_{-\infty}^{\infty} b_n \, e(nt)$$

then for x fixed

$$h(x - t)^* \sim \sum_{-\infty}^{\infty} [b_n \, e(nx)]^* \, e(nt).$$

Proof. We have

$$\frac{1}{2\pi} \int_{}^{\pi} h(x - t)^* \, e(- nt) \, dt = \frac{1}{2\pi} \int_{x-\pi}^{x+\pi} h(u)^* \, e(n\{u - x\}) \, du$$

$$= \frac{1}{2\pi} \int_{-\pi}^{\pi} h(u)^* \, e(n\{u - x\}) \, du$$

$$= e(- nx) \frac{1}{2\pi} \int_{-\pi}^{\pi} h(u)^* \, e(nu) \, du$$

$$= e(- nx) \frac{1}{2\pi} \left[\int_{-\pi}^{\pi} h(u) \, e(- nu) \, du \right]^*$$

$$= e(- nx) \, b_n^*.$$

LEMMA 4b. If $h, g \in \mathfrak{F}^c$ and if

$$h(x) \sim \sum_{-\infty}^{\infty} b_n \, e(nx), \qquad g(x) \sim \sum_{-\infty}^{\infty} a_n \, e(nx),$$

then

(**7**) $$\qquad h \star g \cdot (x) = \sum_{-\infty}^{\infty} b_n \, a_n \, e(nx) \qquad (-\infty < x < \infty).$$

Proof. Note that in (**7**) we have " $=$ " not " \sim "! We have

$$g(t) \sim \sum_{-\infty}^{\infty} a_n \, e(nt),$$

$$h(x - t)^* \sim \sum_{-\infty}^{\infty} \{b_n^* \, e(- nx)\} \, e(nt).$$

By Theorem 3d we find that, since $h(x - t)^{**} = h(x - t)$,

$$\frac{1}{2\pi} \int_{-\pi}^{\pi} g(t) \, h(x - t) \, dt = \sum_{-\infty}^{\infty} a_n \{b_n^* \, e(-nx)\}^*$$

$$= \sum_{-\infty}^{\infty} b_n \, a_n \, e(nx),$$

as desired.

THEOREM 4c. If $h, g \in \mathfrak{F}^c$ and if

$$h(x) \sim \sum_{-\infty}^{\infty} b_n \, e(nx), \qquad g(x) \sim \sum_{-\infty}^{\infty} a_n \, e(nx),$$

then

1. $\displaystyle \sum_{-\infty}^{\infty} | \, a_n \, | \cdot | \, b_n \, | < \infty$;

2. $h \star g \cdot (x) \in \mathfrak{F}^c \cap \mathfrak{C}$;

3. $\displaystyle h \star g \sim \sum_{-\infty}^{\infty} b_n \, a_n \, e(nx)$.

Proof. We shall begin by proving Conclusion 1. By Bessel's inequality in complex form (see Sec. 7 of Chapter 3), we have

$$\sum_{-\infty}^{\infty} | \, a_n \, |^2 < \infty, \qquad \sum_{-\infty}^{\infty} | \, b_n \, |^2 < \infty.$$

Using the inequality

$$0 \leq | \, a_n \, | \cdot | \, b_n \, | \leq \tfrac{1}{2} | \, a_n \, |^2 + \tfrac{1}{2} | \, b_n \, |^2$$

and the comparison test, Theorem 5a of Chapter 1, we find that

$$\sum_{-\infty}^{\infty} | \, a_n \, | \, | \, b_n \, | < \infty,$$

and Conclusion 1 is proved. Since $| \, e(x) \, | \leq 1$ for all x,

$$| \, b_n \, a_n \, e(nx) \, | \leq | \, b_n \, | \cdot | \, a_n \, |.$$

By the complex analogue[1] of the Weierstrass uniform comparison test, Theorem 2h of Chapter 4, we see that the series

$$\sum_{-\infty}^{\infty} b_n \, a_n \, e(nx)$$

converges uniformly for $-\infty < x < \infty$. The complex analogue of Theorem 2a of Chapter 4 then shows that the sum $h \star g \cdot (x)$ of this series is continuous. Thus $h \star g \in \mathfrak{F}^c \cap \mathfrak{C}$ and Conclusion 2 is proved.
Finally

$$\frac{1}{2\pi} \int_{-\pi}^{\pi} h \star g \cdot (x) \, e(-nx) \, dx = \frac{1}{2\pi} \int_{-\pi}^{\pi} \left\{ \sum_{m=-\infty}^{\infty} b_m \, a_m \, e(mx) \right\} e(-nx) \, dx$$

$$= \frac{1}{2\pi} \sum_{m=-\infty}^{\infty} \int_{-\pi}^{\pi} b_m \, a_m \, e(mx) \, e(-nx) \, dx$$

by the complex analogue of Theorem 2f of Chapter 4. Since

$$\frac{1}{2\pi} \int_{-\pi}^{\pi} e(mx) \, e(-nx) \, dx = \begin{cases} 0 & (m \neq n) \\ 1 & (m = n), \end{cases}$$

we find that

$$\frac{1}{2\pi} \int_{-\pi}^{\pi} h \star g(x) \, e(-nx) = b_n \, a_n \,,$$

and our proof is complete.

[1] The complex analogues of several results proved only in the real case are used here. These results can be deduced from the corresponding real results by the simple device of considering real and imaginary parts separately.

Appendix

1. Set and Sequence Operations

In this section we define and develop the basic properties of "least upper bound," "limit superior," "Cauchy sequence," etc.

If the real numbers \Re have been defined (for example as certain equivalence classes of rational numbers), the result below can be proved as a theorem. Our procedure will be to assume it as an axiom and then to use it in order to deduce further properties of \Re.

AXIOM 1a. Let s_n ($n \in \mathfrak{P}$) satisfy:

1. s_n is nondecreasing (nonincreasing); that is,

$$s_0 \le s_1 \le s_2 \le \cdots \quad (s_0 \ge s_1 \ge s_2 \ge \cdots);$$

2. s_n is bounded from above (below); that is, there is a constant M such that $s_n \le M, n \in \mathfrak{P}$ ($s_n \ge M, n \in \mathfrak{P}$); then $\lim_{n \to \infty} s_n$ exists.

The above consists of two statements, one about nondecreasing sequences bounded from above, and one about nonincreasing sequences bounded from below. Either of these statements implies the other, see Problem 1, so that instead of assuming both statements, it would be enough to assume either one.

Let $S \subset \Re$ be a set of real numbers. Then $a \in \Re$ is said to be an upper (lower) bound for S if for every $x \in S$, we have $x \le a$ ($x \ge a$). For example, 10 is an upper bound for $\{1, 2, 3\}$. Not every set S has an upper bound; the set $\{0 \le x < \infty\}$ does not have an upper bound. Let $S \subset R$. Now a is said to be a least upper (greatest lower) bound for S if a is an upper (lower) bound of S and if no other upper (lower) bound is smaller (larger). It is immediately evident that if a_1 and a_2 are both least upper bounds for the same set S, then $a_1 = a_2$. This is because $a_2 \ge a_1$ and $a_1 \le a_2$. Consequently we can speak of *the* least upper bound if one exists, etc. The least upper bound of a set S is designated by "l.u.b. S" and the greatest lower bound by "g.l.b. S."

THEOREM 1b. Every nonempty subset S of \Re which has an upper (lower) bound has a least upper (greatest lower) bound.

Proof. We deduce the first statement from Axiom 1a. Let S have upper bound M. For each integer $n \in \mathfrak{P}$ let t_n be the smallest number of the form $m/2^n$, where m is an integer, which is an upper bound for S. Then $t_0 \ge t_1 \ge \cdots$,

and the $\{t_n\}_0^\infty$ are bounded from below by *any* element of S. Thus by Axiom 1a, t_n converges to a limit t. Here t is an upper bound of S (see Problem 2). A simple argument (left to the reader) shows that if t' is any upper bound of S, then $t \leq t_n \leq t' + 2^{-n}$ for $n = 0, 1, 2, \cdots$ so that $t \leq t'$.

If we adopt the conventions

$$\text{l.u.b. } \varnothing = -\infty,$$

$$\text{g.l.b. } \varnothing = +\infty,$$

$$\text{l.u.b. } S = +\infty \qquad \text{if } S \neq \varnothing \text{ has no upper bound,}$$

$$\text{g.l.b. } S = -\infty \qquad \text{if } S \neq \varnothing \text{ has no lower bound,}$$

then least upper bound and greatest lower bound are defined for every set S.

Let $u_n (n \in \mathfrak{P})$ be given. We define

(1)

$$\overline{\lim_{n \to \infty}} \, u_n = \text{l.u.b. } \{x \mid x < u_n \text{ for infinitely many } n\},$$

$$\underline{\lim_{n \to \infty}} \, u_n = \text{g.l.b. } \{x \mid x > u_n \text{ for infinitely many } n\}.$$

The symbols $\overline{\lim}$ and $\underline{\lim}$ are read "limit superior" and "limit inferior," respectively.

Theorem 1c. Let u_n $(n \in \mathfrak{P})$ be given. There is a subsequence u_{n_k} of u_n such that

(2)

$$\lim_{k \to \infty} u_{n_k} = \overline{\lim_{n \to \infty}} \, u_n.$$

Moreover no subsequence of u_n converges to a limit greater than $\overline{\lim_{n \to \infty}} \, u_n$.

Similarly there is a subsequence u_{m_j} of u_n such that

$$\lim_{j \to \infty} u_{m_j} = \underline{\lim_{n \to \infty}} \, u_n,$$

and no subsequence of u_n converges to a limit smaller than $\underline{\lim} \, u_n$.

When $\overline{\lim_{n \to \infty}} \, u_n$ is not finite, this theorem must be given the following interpretation. If $\overline{\lim_{n \to \infty}} \, u_n = +\infty$, there exists a subsequence u_{n_k} with the property that given any T there is an index k_0 such that $u_{n_k} > T$ if $k \geq k_0$. If $\overline{\lim_{n \to \infty}} \, u_n = -\infty$, there exists a subsequence u_{n_k} with the property that given any T, there is any index k_0 such that $u_{n_k} < T$ if $k \geq k_0$.

Proof. We shall consider only the case $\overline{\lim_{n \to \infty}} \, u_n = s$ (s finite). By definition given $\epsilon > 0$, there are infinitely many u_n's $> s - \epsilon$ but only finitely many u_n's $> s + \epsilon$. Consequently infinitely many u_n's lie in the interval $s - \epsilon < x <$

$s + \epsilon$. Thus there is an index n_0 such that $s - 2^0 < u_{n_0} < s + 2^0$; there is an index $n_1 > n_0$ such that $s - 2^{-1} < u_{n_1} < s + 2^{-1}$; there is an index $n_2 > n_1$ such that $s - 2^{-2} < u_{n_2} < s + 2^{-2}$; etc. Clearly $\lim_{k \to \infty} u_{n_k} = s$. It is obvious that no subsequence can converge to a limit greater than s.

THEOREM 1d. Let u_n, $v_n (n \in \mathfrak{P})$ be given. Then[1]

1. $\varlimsup_{n \to \infty} (u_n + v_n) \le \varlimsup_{n \to \infty} u_n + \varlimsup_{n \to \infty} v_n$,

2. $\varlimsup_{n \to \infty} (u_n + v_n) \ge \varlimsup_{n \to \infty} u_n + \varliminf_{n \to \infty} v_n$,

3. $\varlimsup_{n \to \infty} (u_n + v_n) = \varlimsup_{n \to \infty} u_n + \lim_{n \to \infty} v_n$ if $\lim_{n \to \infty} v_n$ exists.

If in addition $u_n \ge 0$, $v_n \ge 0$ $(n \in \mathfrak{P})$, then

4. $\varlimsup_{n \to \infty} (u_n \, v_n) \le \varlimsup_{n \to \infty} u_n \cdot \varlimsup_{n \to \infty} v_n$,

5. $\varlimsup_{n \to \infty} (u_n \, v_n) \ge \varlimsup_{n \to \infty} u_n \cdot \varliminf_{n \to \infty} v_n$,

6. $\varlimsup_{n \to \infty} (u_n \, v_n) = \varlimsup_{n \to \infty} u_n \cdot \lim_{n \to \infty} v_n$ if $\lim_{n \to \infty} v_n$ exists.

Proof. Given $\epsilon > 0$, all but finitely many u_n's are less than $\varlimsup_{n \to \infty} u_n + \epsilon$, and all but finitely many v_n's are less than $\varlimsup_{n \to \infty} v_n + \epsilon$. Therefore all but finitely many $(u_n + v_n)$'s are less than $\varlimsup_{n \to \infty} u_n + \varlimsup_{n \to \infty} v_n + 2\epsilon$. Conclusion 1 now follows. Given $\epsilon > 0$, infinitely many u_n's are greater than $\varlimsup_{n \to \infty} u_n - \epsilon$, and all but finitely many v_n's are greater than $\varliminf_{n \to \infty} v_n - \epsilon$. Thus infinitely many $(u_n + v_n)$'s are greater than $\varlimsup_{n \to \infty} u_n + \varliminf_{n \to \infty} v_n - 2\epsilon$ which proves Conclusion 2. Finally Conclusion 3 is a consequence of Conclusions 1 and 2 since if $\lim_{n \to \infty} v_n$ exists, then

$$\varlimsup_{n \to \infty} v_n = \varliminf_{n \to \infty} v_n = \lim_{n \to \infty} v_n, \text{ etc.}$$

The following result follows from Theorem 1c.

COROLLARY 1e. Let $u_n (n \in \mathfrak{P})$ be a bounded sequence; that is, there exists constants $-\infty < a < b < \infty$ such that $a \le u_n \le b$ for $n \in \mathfrak{P}$. Then there exists a subsequence u_{n_k} of u_n and a number u, $a \le u \le b$, such that $\lim_{k \to \infty} u_{n_k} = u$.

A sequence $s_n (n \in \mathfrak{P})$ is said to be a *Cauchy sequence* if given any $\epsilon > 0$, there is an index N such that

$$|s_n - s_m| < \epsilon \qquad \text{if } n, m \ge N.$$

THEOREM 1f. Every convergent sequence is a Cauchy sequence and every Cauchy sequence is a convergent sequence.

[1] In Conclusions 1–3 the only cases which must be excluded are those for which the right-hand side would reduce to $(\infty) + (-\infty)$. In Conclusions 4–6 the only cases which must be excluded are those for which the right-hand side would reduce to $0 \cdot (\infty)$.

Proof. If $\lim_{n \to \infty} s_n = s$, then given $\epsilon > 0$ there is an index N such that $|s_n - s| < \epsilon/2$ if $n \geq N$. If $m, n \geq N$, then

$$|s_n - s_m| = |(s_n - s) - (s_m - s)| \leq |s_n - s| + |s_m - s|$$
$$< \frac{\epsilon}{2} + \frac{\epsilon}{2} = \epsilon,$$

which proves our first assertion. Next let $s_n(n \in \mathfrak{P})$ be a Cauchy sequence. It is almost immediate that this implies that $\{s_n\}_0^\infty$ is bounded. By Corollary 1e there exists a subsequence s_{n_k} converging to a limit s. Now use Problem 4.

PROBLEMS

1. Prove that either of the statements below implies the other:

(a) every nondecreasing sequence bounded from above is convergent;

(b) every nonincreasing sequence bounded from below is convergent.

2. Let S be a nonempty subset of \mathfrak{R}. Show that if $\{t_n\}_0^\infty$ are all upper bounds for S and if $\lim_{n \to \infty} t_n = t$ exists, then t is an upper bound for S.

3. Prove directly from the definition of "$\underline{\lim}$" and "$\overline{\lim}$" that if $\underline{\lim}\, u_n = \overline{\lim}_{n \to \infty} u_n = s$ where s is finite, then $\lim_{n \to \infty} u_n = s$, and conversely.

4. Prove directly from the definition that if $\{s_n\}_0^\infty$ is a Cauchy sequence and if $\lim_{k \to \infty} s_{n_k} = s$ where s_{n_k} is a subsequence of s_n, then $\lim_{n \to \infty} s_n = s$.

5. Prove that if $\{s_n\}_0^\infty$ is nondecreasing and bounded, it is Cauchy. Deduce from this that if Theorem 1f is assumed as an "axiom," Axiom 1a can be proved as a "theorem."

2. Continuous Functions

In this section we define continuity and deduce those properties of continuous functions which we have occasion to use.

DEFINITION 2a. Let S be a subset of \mathfrak{R}, and let $f(x)$ be a real valued function defined on S. Now $f(x)$ is said to be continuous at a point $x_0 \in S$ if given $\epsilon > 0$ there is a $\delta > 0$ such that $|f(x) - f(x_0)| < \epsilon$ for $x \in S$ and $|x - x_0| < \delta$. f is continuous on S if it is continuous at each point of S.

LEMMA 2b. Let $\{u_n\}_1^\infty$ be a convergent sequence, $\lim_{n \to \infty} u_n = u$. Let $f(x)$ be a function defined on a set S, and let $u_n \in S$ $(n = 1, 2, \cdots)$ and $u \in S$. If f is continuous at u, then

(1)
$$\lim_{n \to \infty} f(u_n) = f(u).$$

Proof. Left to the reader.

THEOREM 2c. If $f(x)$ is defined and continuous for $a \le x \le b$, then

$$M = \text{l.u.b. } \{f(x) \mid a \le x \le b\} < \infty,$$

and there is a point $x_M (a = x_M \le b)$ such that $f(x_M) = M$. Similarly

$$m = \text{g.l.b. } \{f(x) \mid a \le x \le b\} > -\infty,$$

and there is a point $x_m (a \le x_m \le b)$ such that $f(x_m) = m$.

Proof. Let $M = \text{l.u.b. } \{f(x) \mid a \le x \le b\}$. Now M is either a finite number or $+\infty$. In any event there exists a sequence $\{x_n\}_1^\infty$ of points $a \le x_n \le b$ (not necessarily distinct) such that[1] $\lim_{n\to\infty} f(x_n) = M$. By Corollary 1e, $\{x_n\}_1^\infty$ contains a subsequence x_{n_k} $(k = 0, 1, 2, \cdots)$ converging to a limit x_M $(a \le x_M \le b)$.

We have
$$\lim_{k\to\infty} f(x_{n_k}) = M,$$

but since f is continuous at x_M, Lemma 2b implies that

$$\lim_{k\to\infty} f(x_{n_k}) = f(x_M).$$

Thus $f(x_M) = M$. Since $f(x_M)$ is finite, so is M, etc.

THEOREM 2d. If $f(x)$ is continuous for $a \le x \le b$ and if $f(a) = A$, $f(b) = B$, then for any number C lying between A and B there is a number c lying between a and b such that $f(c) = C$.

Proof. Let us assume for the sake of definiteness that $A < C < B$. Let $S = \{x \mid a \le x \le b, f(x) \le C\}$, and let $c = \text{l.u.b. } S$. We shall prove that $f(c) = C$. Since f is continuous at $x = c$ and since by the construction of c every interval $c - \delta \le x \le c$ contains points for which $f(x) \le C$, it follows that $f(c) \le C$. Again every interval $c \le x \le c + \delta$ consists entirely of points x for which $f(x) \ge C$, and thus $f(c) \ge C$. Q.E.D.

We refer the reader to Sec. 2 of Chapter 7 for the definition of uniform continuity.

THEOREM 2e. If $f(x)$ is continuous at each point of the finite closed interval $\{a \le x \le b\}$, it is uniformly continuous there.

Proof. We must show that for each $\epsilon > 0$ there is a $\delta > 0$ such that if $x', x'' \in \{a \le x \le b\}$ and if $|x' - x''| < \delta$, then $|f(x') - f(x'')| < \epsilon$. Suppose that for a given ϵ no such δ exists. Let $\delta_n = 2^{-n}(b - a)$ $(n = 1, 2, \cdots)$. For each δ_n there would then exist points $x'_n, x''_n \in \{a \le x \le b\}$ such that $|x'_n - x''_n| < \delta_n$ and such that $|f(x'_n) - f(x''_n)| > \epsilon$. By Corollary 1e there is then a subsequence

[1] If $M = \infty$, this is to be interpreted to mean that for every (large positive) number T there is an index n_0 such that $f(x_n) > T$ if $n \ge n_0$.

x'_{n_k} ($k = 1, 2, \cdots$) of x'_n ($n = 1, 2, \cdots$) which is convergent to a point $y \in \{a \le x \le b\}$. Since f is continuous at y, there is a number $\eta > 0$ such that if $|x - y| < \eta$, then $|f(y) - f(x)| < \epsilon/2$. For k sufficiently large we would have $|y - x'_{n_k}| < \eta$ and $|y - x''_{n_k}| < \eta$. But then

$$|f(x'_{n_k}) - f(x''_{n_k})| \le |f(x'_{n_k}) - f(y)| + |f(x''_k) - f(y)| < \epsilon.$$

This however is a contradiction.

PROBLEMS

1. Let $f(x)$ be defined and continuous on a set $S \subset \mathfrak{R}$. Let S_1 be a subset of S, and let $f_1(x)$ be the restriction of $f(x)$ to the set S_1. Show that $f_1(x)$ is continuous on S_1.

2. Prove that if $f(x)$ and $g(x)$ are continuous functions on a set S, then so is:

(a) $af(x)$ for any $a \in \mathfrak{R}$;
(b) $f(x) + g(x)$;
(c) $f(x) g(x)$.

3. Prove that if $p(x) = a_0 + a_1 x + \cdots + a_n x^n$ is any polynomial (with real coefficients), then $p(x)$ is continuous on \mathfrak{R}. HINT: First prove that the function $f(x) = x$ is continuous, and then use Problem 2.

4. Let $f(x)$ be a continuous function on a set S, and $F(x)$ a continuous function on a set T. Show that if $f(x) \in T$ for every $x \in S$ so that $F[f(x)]$ is defined for every $x \in S$, then $F[f(x)]$ is continuous for $x \in S$.

5. Let f be a function defined on a set $S \subset \mathfrak{R}$, and let $u \in S$. Show that if for every sequence $\{u_n\}_1^\infty$ of points in S converging to u, $\lim_{n \to \infty} u_n = u$, we have $\lim_{n \to \infty} f(u_n) = f(u)$, then f is continuous at u.

6. Prove that if $f(x)$ is a piecewise continuous function on a finite interval $a \le x \le b$ (see Definition 1a of Chapter 3), then $M = \text{l.u.b.} \{f(x) \mid a \le x \le b\}$ is finite. Does there always exist a number $x_M(a \le x_M \le b)$ such that $f(x_M) = M$? Justify your answer.

Index
Index of Symbols

Index

Index of Symbols

173